MY VOYAGE THROUGH LIFE AND MEDICINE

Forty Years of Change—Are We Better Off Today?

JORGE ROJAS-BRASSETTI, MD

My Voyage through Life and Medicine: Forty Years of Change—Are We Better Off Today?

ISBN-13: 978-1-5052-0755-2
ISBN-10: 150520755X

DEDICATION

When I started to write this book, I wanted to dedicate it to the people who were responsible for how I have lived my life. The same six people always come to my mind, probably because all of them had such a profound influence on my life and career: *Marta Brassetti de Rojas (my mother), Jose Tomas Rojas Symonds (my father), Jose Tomas (Pepe) Rojas Brassetti (my brother), and Alexander (Sandy) W. Pierce, and Mildred (Millie) Stahlman (my professors)*.

My mother taught me that it does not matter where you look, for there is beauty all around us even in the simplest things; my father was the hardest-working physician I have ever known. At night when he tucked me in bed, he used to ask me if I had learned something. If I said no, he would always say, "You wasted a day!" Pepe, my brother, was responsible for my going to medical school; I guess his white uniform and the enthusiasm he seemed to have for his career were big selling points. Sandy got me started on the path of pediatrics and taught me that I could make any diagnosis if I believed in my knowledge and clinical skills, and Millie reinforced my clinical skills, and taught me that it is only through careful research that we can advance the practice of medicine. Sandy and Millie always agreed on one simple fact: the patient will always tell you the diagnosis; all you need to do is observe, examine, and ask the right questions. The laboratory, the X-rays, and the consultants should be there only to confirm it.

My father also taught me that, in most cases, the patient gets better with, without, and in spite of the doctor.

Finally to my wife of forty-four years, *Angela del Valle*, who has stood by me through thick and thin and through the years has put up with all my eccentricities and temper tantrums!

I will forever be thankful for what they taught me and for their being part of my life.

My mother once told me that we never go through life alone: "God always sends somebody to guide us through." As always she was right!

CONTENTS

FOREWORD

Dr. Jorge Rojas is a man for all seasons. I met this renaissance character in 1979 on my first rotation as an intern at Vanderbilt Hospital. Initially he was one of the neonatal fellows and then became one of my attending physicians. We occupied a very strange microcosm of the universe known as the Neonatal Intensive Care Unit. People who have not traveled here cannot really comprehend it. He and I would come to live in this small universe for the next thirty-five-plus years along with a cast of characters that include some of the best people the world has to offer.

I refer to him as a renaissance man. Dr. Rojas has described here in this book much about his life as a clinician, researcher, teacher, manager, mentor, father, husband, grief counselor, tech guru, and computer whiz. He does not include the part of his life that involves music, song writing and performance, horsemanship, horse training, farming, and bush-hogger extraordinaire! There may be even more skills and talents that I still do not know.

I worked with Jorge as a partner in our neonatology practice for thirty years in addition to being under his tutelage during my training. I am very thankful for this good fortune. Because of his excellence as a clinician and his profound knowledge base, I had the opportunity to be constantly pulled forward, though sometimes reluctantly. (I do not possess the driving force of his work ethic or his profound intellect.)

I have to admit that many things about Jorge in this book are new to me. I knew when I arrived at Baptist hospital in 1985 that the nurses were of high caliber, but I didn't stop to dwell on the question of how their skills were developed. The "2-4-1" neonatal resuscitation program Jorge created and fully implemented among the entire NICU/OB staff was already in place, many years preceding the institution on the AAP Neonatal Resuscitation Program. I was impressed by the deeply compassionate formalized grief support offered to families experiencing loss. It was cutting edge and put in place before hospice became mainstream. The nurses then taught me what I did not know or even imagine: the deep and even personal knowledge and the extensive research involved in developing and implementing these programs. The fact that I did not know is evidence that Jorge is a humble and private man.

This book is thoughtful, candid, and wise. It is also an excellently researched critical analysis of what has happened to health care from a very astute combatant on the battlefield. I think this is a very valuable addition to the dialogue of what needs to happen to our health care system in order to pull it back on the rails before it is too late.

Additionally, this is a good example of what a life looks like when following a true vocation. The theologian Frederick Buechner describes vocation as the place where the soul's deep gladness meets the world's great need. It is a special minority who get to follow their true vocation. Perhaps another way to think of this is as a "calling," if you are more religiously inclined. In many ways Dr. Rojas' mother was prescient when she sewed priest garments for the serious young boy you are going to meet in these pages. Even at an early age, he had a thirst to do good.

Elizabeth Krueger, MD

PREFACE

Writing about one's own life may seem to be presumptuous. It may not have been so if I had been a witness to or participated in great historical events, or had done something extraordinary. But that is not the case; I have lived an ordinary life, similar to that of thousands of people, and I am sure that many have lives more interesting than mine. The only difference in my case is that I started medicine at a time and place where fee for service was the rule and the relationship between patient and doctor was very personal. Unfortunately, through the next forty years, medicine, or health care as we call it now, has changed into an impersonal regulated industry that in no way follows the Hippocratic oath I took when I became a doctor. I believe this is worth writing about.

How did we get here? Are we better off today? These are questions to which each person probably has a different answer. You the reader, will have to find your own. I can only provide you with the experiences I lived through on my journey. I created my own path in medicine, I followed my passion, and stuck to it until things changed so much that I forced myself into retirement. It was a difficult decision, but one that I found necessary. Do I miss medicine? I do and will probably do so till I die.

I had many mentors throughout my life, and I am thankful to each and every one of them. All the advice and support that I received from them molded who I became. I also love to help others; I love mentoring, I love teaching, and I love to write. I am finally getting to do what I wanted to do for years. Even though I wrote and published several scientific papers in my career writing a book was always at the back of my mind. I hope this book will help others find their path through their careers.

My specialty is pediatrics and my subspecialty, neonatology. Even though I was exposed to many other specialties throughout my life, I do not pretend to know what goes on outside my world. I have been a doctor and a parent and a patient; what I write is what I have seen and experienced myself. Some may not agree with the way I see things, but I hope that at least this book may cause people to reexamine health care not only in the light of what we have accomplished but also in regard to what we have lost.

Throughout the book I will refer to people only by their first names, I think this is the best way to do it. If by any chance they get to read this book, they will know I am referring to them. It will be up to them to choose to tell others that I mentioned them. I will refer to the institutions that I worked and trained in by their official names. Each one of them was part of my life, and I have very fond memories of all of them.

1973 –The Hippocratic Oath

Chapter 1
THE LAUNCH

My life started in March 1948. I was born in Mexico City to wonderful parents and into an even more wonderful family. I had two older brothers and eventually a younger sister, whom I initially resented, since she claimed the baby's position that I had enjoyed for five years. But I love them all! My early childhood was better than average; I was fortunate to have a mother who taught me to appreciate the small things in life and encouraged me to follow my desire to learn to play music, which eventually would become a very important part of my life. I attended a private school, where I became what nowadays would be considered a nerd. In elementary and middle school, I did not play any sports, but I managed to always be at the top of my class.

Then something happened when I hit middle school, which in Mexico is called secondary school. I am not sure if it was hormones, or the fact that all my friends were only interested in impressing the girls—I started playing sports. I found out I was not such a bad soccer player; I even made the varsity team, but was not good enough to impress anybody.

So by the time I started high school, I decided to do something different. I had learned to play the guitar when I was five; actually, my oldest brother was the one who took the lessons, and I just learned some things from him, but mostly by myself. Music always came easy to me, and it was always a helpful thing to know. It was my secret weapon! So I started a rock band and called myself the musical director! Unfortunately, my friends were not very good players, but they were all willing to learn and I was willing to teach. For the first time in my life, I learned how to deal with four different personalities and make things simple and easy to understand; this skill would help me throughout my life.

It took about four months of meetings and long rehearsals, always in the living room of my house, which my mother was nice enough to let us use. Finally on September 24, 1965, I, Georges, Juan, Juan Ismael, and Jesus became the "Nowheremen" and played our first gig. By then, we had learned fifteen songs, and we knew we were ready for our debut.

It was instant success; from there we got invited to play at parties almost every weekend, and eventually we even got paid to do it. I was finally a popular guy! The next two years became one of the best experiences of my life. I had to quickly learn how to deal with people, manage money, and I even did some marketing! I absolutely loved it, even when Juan announced he was quitting the band, and we had to replace him.

I was not ready for auditions! The band had been formed by friends; I had nightmares about bringing somebody in who would not fit. Fortunately, out of *nowhere*, no pun intended, Pablo showed up, and he was a perfect fit, so the band went on without a hitch.

In July of 1967, we entered a TV contest called Fanáticos a Go-Go; it was your usual battle of the bands of the '60s. On our first night we sang our two best songs and made it through to the next session; we were ecstatic, and our parents were pleasantly surprised. A week later in the second session—we won again! We knew we had a chance to win the whole thing, so we rehearsed every day, and on July 29, we won the final! We were on top of the world; we won a two-year recording contract with Orfeon Records in Mexico. But we were all at the end of preparatory school, and it was time to decide on a career, which we all knew was not going to be music, so we turned down the contract, and a few months later on March 9, 1968 the group dissolved never to play again.

But as exciting and important as those years were in my life, they are not the purpose of this book, although they form an important part of the background. It is just to let the reader know what my life was like before entering medical school. What I would like to emphasize here are the changes in the medical field as they happened during the different stages of my life: from the young, intrepid medical student to the old and tired neonatologist.

This book represents more than forty years during which the meaning of being a physician changed dramatically. So I will continue by answering the first question: Why did I become a doctor?

Most people would respond, "Because I wanted to help people." Well, in addition to that; I got into medicine because it was what I knew. My grandfather, my father, and my brother were doctors; I was comfortable with what they did. I knew how their lives had been and how they seemed to be satisfied and happy with their careers. If they did it, I knew I could do it.

To tell the truth, it was not always that way. Throughout my younger years I wanted to be many things, but the one that I remember the best was wanting to be a priest when I was ten years old. I was born and raised Catholic and probably had been influenced by a very religious mother who encouraged my feelings.

Throughout my life, I had a vivid imagination and always wanted to live things for real. When I wanted to be a priest, I asked my mother to make me a set of priest vestments; she, who did not know how to do anything half way, a trait that I found out I inherited, sewed a complete set: from the alb to a beautiful green chasuble. She even got me a white cincture, an amice, and a matching stole. I learned the parts of the mass and pretended to celebrate mass and even gave homilies, usually to my mother or my younger sister who would sit through my service just to get to Communion, which was usually a piece of candy. This idea was very short lived, since as I mentioned before, as soon as I turned twelve and entered middle school, I started to notice girls, and the thought of priesthood quickly vanished.

My next and probably longest career ambition was to be a veterinarian. As I was growing up, my grandfather, Nicolás, exposed me to colombofilia or pigeon-fancying, which is the breeding and training of homer pigeons, and training them into racing pigeons, which can fly back home from distant points. I saved money and bought a pair of pigeons, and from them I eventually had a full pigeon house of them. Starting with a small pigeon house, I eventually had one that I could walk into. Unfortunately, I never raced my pigeons much, even though most of the time they would come home. I was so afraid of losing them that I quit doing it. This launched my desire to make animal care a career; I had no idea what a veterinarian really did, but I was sure I wanted to be one. This thought stayed with me through high school and up to a few weeks before veterinary school started. I even tried my hand at raising chicks and ducklings; unfortunately, my mother thought that the only purpose to raising chickens was to eat them, so all my successes always ended up on our dinner table. Only, Clodoveo and Cleopatra, my only two successes with ducks were saved by my pleas and lived their life in our backyard till old age took them.

I should explain now that the Mexican educational system is somewhat different. After six years of elementary school and three years of middle (secondary) school, we go to preparatory school, which in the United States would be the equivalent of high school. Preparatory school is different from high school in that the level of education is more advanced than that of the US system. Preparatory school is closer to college in the level of teaching, and as its name implies it is a time of preparation for a career. There are three different tracks: physics/mathematics, biology/health, and liberal arts. One has to choose any one after the first year. Since I was going to be a veterinarian, I chose biology/health. Dissecting animals was my most favorite thing to do!

By the end of preparatory school, I had met Georges, the band singer, a good friend and neighbor. His stepfather was an orthopedist; he exposed me to a totally different field of medicine, since my father and grandfather were gastroenterologists. I was fascinated by seeing orthopedic surgery, as well as learning all the different things that were available to mend bones and replace joints, which seemed something I should like to do. So my thoughts of veterinary medicine started fading. Also, I saw my older brother graduate from medical school and move to the United States for a year to do a rotating internship; he looked smashing in his white uniform, and he always seemed to be excited when he came home and told my mother stories about his experiences. I just listened, but there was something in his voice that piqued my curiosity: he seemed to be as satisfied with his budding career, just as my father was after many years of practice.

It was 1966 and the end of my third year of preparatory school. The time had come to apply to the University of Mexico (UNAM), so I submitted my application to the School of Veterinary Medicine.

In a couple of weeks I received my acceptance letter to veterinary school, which was not surprising. I had finished school fourth in my class, with a grade average of 94 (out of 100). I should have been ecstatic, but deep inside me I was not; I thought maybe I should have applied to medical school instead. Medicine was what I knew, and what my grandfather, father, and brother did. I knew that their lives had been full of satisfaction and that all of them never seemed to have regretted their decision. All of a sudden, I went into a panic; I was convinced that treating animals would not be as fulfilling as taking care of humans; I wanted to be a doctor!

With much fear, I confided in my father, and to my surprise he was not mad, but ecstatic that I wanted to follow in his footsteps like my oldest brother had. At that time, he was a clinical professor in the UNAM, and my grandfather was a member of the university's medical examiners, so they were well connected. He made a few phone calls and told me not to worry. To this date I do not know how he did it or who helped him, but he asked me to keep it a secret and so I did. This is the first time I have ever talked about it since it happened in 1966. Two weeks later I received my letter of acceptance to the UNAM Medical School, the same school my father and brother had attended.

I want to spend some time at this point explaining that things were very different in Mexico than they were in the United States when I was growing up. In Mexico, the children of physicians are never singled out in school as being different; I never heard phrases like "his dad is a doctor" or "he must be rich" as my children did. Undoubtedly, doctors had an aura that made them different, but this aura was not one of envy, but one of respect. Nobody questioned the preeminence of the medical profession. Even though socialized medicine was growing in Mexico, the traditional fee-for-service, family-doctor-at-the-bedside model was still the norm. My grandfather and my father were doctors, but in those days even though physicians made a decent living, their incomes were hardly sizeable.

Both my grandfather and my father were gastroenterologists and worked very hard. For many years they both co-owned a pharmacy, so on top of their gastroenterology private practice, which was located downtown, they managed the pharmacy, supervised a full-time pharmacist, who prepared all the compound medications (which were many in those days), and made sure that deliveries were done on time (prescription medications were often delivered at home). Running the pharmacy was practically a full-time job, and they still managed to have their private practice. Eventually, the pharmacy became more of a burden than a profitable endeavor, so they sold it and continued with their private practice, which was also beginning to dwindle because of the growth of institutionalized medicine in Mexico.

My father eventually had to join institutionalized medicine and started working at the Mexican Social Security Institute (IMSS) during the day. This was a much more demanding job; he worked three hours at a clinic in the mornings and then did one hour doing home visits. He would come home for lunch and then go back to the clinic, where he would work another three hours and then do one more hour of home visits. When he was done at the IMSS, he would join my grandfather at his private practice office downtown, where he would see more patients and do fluoroscopy studies for another couple of hours. On top of that, twice a week he would stop at a laboratory and read slides from fecal exams, to make some extra money.

Occasionally, as I was growing up, I would go with my father to the clinic and watch him work. He was a character; all the nurses loved him, and he would give hugs and pats in the "back" to many of them. This was never seen as a sign of harassment, but it was accepted with a chuckle as part of his personality. He was well respected by other doctors and always seemed to enjoy his work. He seemed to adapt well to institutionalized medicine, although the pressure of seeing patients every thirty minutes in the clinic setting was sometimes frustrating for him; he missed the freedom of spending more time with some patients as he could do in private practice.

Even though being a doctor's child was nothing special, there were some advantages: When the polio epidemic hit Mexico, we were the first ones to get the Salk and Sabin vaccines, and we had the injections at home while holding our mother's hand. When we needed medications, they were immediately supplied by the pharmacy, or my father would bring them home himself. Most of all, we were indelibly and positively marked by our exposure to the noblest of professions. I have no idea if my children feel the same way, but I hope they do. I always felt a bit special. Not arrogant or superior or better, but proud!

Chapter 2
MEDICAL SCHOOL

I will have to say that going to medical school was a bit scary at the beginning. I was leaving behind all my high school buddies, some whom I had been with since first grade, and going to a new school where I did not know anybody.

About six weeks before school started, we had to go and pick up our schedules and find out which group we would be in during the first semester. I was going to be in group 601; my schedule included anatomy, cadaver dissection, embryology, and introduction to public health. The same day, I got to meet several people who were going to be in my group: Juan, Enrique, Miguel, and Manuel were four of them; we did not know then that we would become very good friends and remain together till graduation and beyond.

We dreaded the first day of medical school. In Mexico, traditionally, first-year students at the UNAM are considered *perros* (dogs) and hazing goes on, as it has for as long as I can remember. My father was hazed as well as my brother; they both lost their hair the first day of school. It was no different for me; as soon as we were recognized as perros, a crowd of students approached us, and once we accepted we were first-year students, they cut and carved our hair. Most of the time, if you are submissive and allow the second-year students to cut your hair and then spend the first few days with your head "carved" there was no problem; I kept my hair as they left it for the first week, and even though I got laughed at many times, I was quite proud to be a perro!

Dr. Mario was our anatomy professor; he was actually an orthopedist, which is not unusual in UNAM. Many teachers are practicing physicians who give some of their time to educate medical students. My own father, a gastroenterologist, used to teach the course Introduction to Clinical Medicine. Fortunately, I did not get to be in his class.

I still remember the impression that Dr. Mario made on us. His first words were "Anatomy is the first filter of many that you will find in your careers. Statistically one-third of you will not get a passing grade. By the end of the semester, you should know every muscle, nerve, organ, vessel, and bone in the human body. If you do not, medicine is not for you." He was right; many of the students in group 601 did not make it past anatomy, not quite a third, but nearly a fourth. Fortunately, God provided me with a good memory, and I did well.

Cadaver dissection was another difficult hurdle to overcome. On the first day of class we were introduced to the cadaver that we would dissect and learn from. We were warned by the professor that we had to stop thinking of our cadaver as a human being, but look at him as learning tool. That was a very hard thing for us to do. In spite of all the advice, we gave him a name, and we graciously named him *Chato*.

I had a difficult time looking at Chato's face. I would cover it while I worked on my assignments. I would go home and think about him all the time. Who was he? How did he end up on our table? Did he have a family? Those are things I will never know, but I will always thank him for allowing me to explore his body for my education.

Another thing that we had to get used to was the smell. Cadavers were preserved by injecting them with formalin, and the smell was very strong. I would go home and still smell the formalin for hours. Even my food would taste the same. Needless to say, by the end of the semester, we had become immune to it, and we would even have lunch in the cadaver lab!

I also had a problem with some of the other students' attitudes; some had lost all respect for their cadavers' humanity and joked and played about their sexual organs, to the point of cutting off a penis and placing it in one of the female students' purses. Even though I will never forget her face when she put her hand in her purse and pulled this thing out, I knew it was wrong. For the first time in my life, I had to stand up and fight for what I believed. Some of my classmates never liked me again when I threatened them with telling the professor, but it felt good to point out what I felt was wrong. On another note, it did give me some brownie points with the girls!

Embryology was fascinating to me; the fact that a new human being would start as two cells and then develop, most of the time, without a glitch into a brand new human being was captivating, I would spend hours looking at the different stages of development, trying to understand how each cell knew where to go and what to develop. There was very little known then about DNA coding, so the growth of a human fetus was mysterious in many ways.

Lastly, in contrast to the other three, Introduction to Public Health was a very boring class. Even though I could see the importance of public health, at this stage of my training this was not what I was craving. I was in a hurry to move on and learn more about the human body's inner workings, which seemed more related to "doctoring" than how the state monitored, regulated, and promoted health care. Little did I know that eventually the state would monitor and regulate medicine in ways I never knew possible.

The semester went fast, and reality set in. I thought I knew exactly what medical school was going to be like, but I was far from right. I was thirsty for some clinical relevance, but I had just spent my first semester memorizing the parts of the body and its development! All of a sudden I realized that it was going to be a while before I was close to a patient. I would have to learn to be patient myself.

The most important thing I learned in my first semester was not from my professors, but my classmates. It was so inspiring to spend every day with people who genuinely wanted to learn. I was amazed by their tenacity and ability to achieve. It motivated me and challenged me keep up with them. Without them, I would probably have never discovered that there were so many ways to study. We would get together and quiz each other, and sometimes one of us would pretend to be the professor. Most of our tests were oral, so we had to prepare differently than we were used to doing in preparatory school. I looked forward to engaging and collaborating with them, but there was also a healthy dose of competition: we all wanted to get the best grade. Even though we all had grades in the high 90s, we still competed with each other. I can vividly remember when Manuel got a 96 in anatomy and I got *only* a 95. I was determined to do better next time.

The second semester, to me, seemed much harder, with biochemistry, physiology, histology, neuroanatomy, and Introduction to Methodology and Statistics. I was excited about the first three; it was all about learning how each part and cell of the body functioned. Unfortunately, neuroanatomy was also there, and we were told it was twice as hard as anatomy; it was supposed to be the second filter we would have to overcome! We had no idea what the last subject was going to be about, but it sounded interesting.

Our biochemistry teacher turned out to be the most boring teacher I ever had. The professor was an overweight man who would sit at his desk and mutter his lectures in the same monotonous voice every day. At the beginning of the semester, I tried very hard to stay awake during his lectures (it was our 7:00 a.m. class), but eventually I decided, and I was not alone, that it was a nice time to take a nap. There were times that I would look around, and many would be doing the same. The test was a multiple-choice written test, so I just convinced myself that I could study from the book and pass it, and so I did.

In contrast, our physiology professor was the most dynamic teacher I had in medical school. He was six feet eight inches tall; he was taller than the blackboard, so on many occasions he would get so excited about a topic that he would start writing on the blackboard and continue to write on the wall above! He made it easier to understand how the human body worked, and what the implications on an individual's health were. His lectures were always exciting, never dull; we all loved to come to listen to him!

He also had an interesting way to keep his class awake; he would break small pieces of chalk and toss them at any student who was snoozing. We were all amazed at his accuracy, and very few tried to sleep through his class.

Histology was interesting; we learned to identify the characteristics of every cell and spent a lot of time looking through a microscope. It was like learning anatomy again, but now down to every minuscule detail of each cell. It was like looking at a universe within a universe! The cells had organs with specific functions, and many were rather specialized. Some were capable of movement, and most amazingly they carried within their nucleuses all the information concerning his or her owner.

The histology final exam was to look through ten different microscopic preparations and identify each cell and its origin. God provided me with a photographic memory, and I aced it!

Neuroanatomy was as advertised the hardest subject ever. I never imagined how complex our brain and nervous system are, but we had a good professor, and his detailed lectures made it easy to understand. Unfortunately, it was a filter; many of my classmates did not make it through. Group 601 had started with forty-one students, and after anatomy and neuroanatomy we were down to twenty-six.

Introduction to Methodology and Statistics was a pleasant surprise. I was sure it would be a boring theory class, but it turned out to be one of the most important classes I ever took. It covered the research methodology and statistics utilized in every single study in medicine, whether basic or clinical research. It was fascinating to me how many ways there were to compare things.

It gave us the tools to understand and judge the medical literature and not just take conclusions for granted. I probably did not grasp, at that time, the importance of statistics; but later in my life I used statistics in my own research and realized that not all that is statistically significant is actually clinically relevant.

The second semester went as fast as the first one, and before we knew it we were second-year medical students never to be called perro again, and it was our turn to haze the perros. Probably the most important thing we learned in the first year was that there was no way around it; we had to continue to study hard if we did not want to be filtered away.

Our second year turned out to be very stimulating. We would finally start to learn a little bit about disease and treatment, as well as tackle some of the subjects in which new knowledge was advancing rapidly, and all was new and exciting: pharmacology, nutrition, pathology, and psychology in the third semester and immunology, genetics, microbiology, and therapeutics in the fourth semester. We also had Introduction to Clinical Medicine, which we attended in small groups throughout the year because it was a short course given by a clinician in a hospital setting. It was our first glimpse at what I thought was "real" medicine with actual patients. Unfortunately, my group was not scheduled to take this short course till almost the end of the year.

Pharmacology and nutrition were not as good as I had expected, even though we discussed how medications were grouped by their effects and how each class worked, it required a lot of memorization. I never had problem memorizing, but it was long and tedious work. In nutrition, we learned the amounts and proportions of protein, fat, and carbohydrates and how to calculate caloric intakes. This was not what I wanted to do; I just could not understand why at this point in my life I had to learn what appeared to be boring recipes. But I must confess that later in my life when I became a neonatologist I was extremely thankful for this knowledge.

Pathology was a fun subject; it was the logical follow up to histology. We had learned to recognize normal cells; now we were learning how they looked when things went wrong. All those images of normal cells that I had stored in my memory were now the basis to recognize disease; I was thankful that my histology professor had insisted that we spend so much time at the microscope looking at normal cells.

Psychology was not for me; I could never get into it, and things like perception, cognition, attention, emotion, intelligence, phenomenology, motivation, personality, behavior, and interpersonal relationships were foreign concepts to me. I could never understand them. I always thought of psychology as a weird subject with a little bit of hocus-pocus; it was certainly not for me. But I worked hard and made it through, not to ever revisit it again in my lifetime.

Now the second semester was a lot of fun, especially immunology and genetics; the information in both subjects was new and exciting. Learning how the human body protects itself against disease and how it adapts to every new challenge was fascinating. But I had a hard time understanding how such a system sometimes attacks itself in the so-called autoimmune disorders or fails to recognize a threat like cancer. Little did I know that what I was studying would continue to change dramatically throughout my career. I always had the feeling that I was permanently a step behind.

Genetics had changed so much in two years! In high school I had learned Mendelian inheritance, a concept developed in the 1800s, using mathematical formulas, on how genetic traits are passed down to descendants, and I was taught the discovery of chromosomes, twenty-three pairs of packages containing all the genetic information. But now we were learning that each chromosome was made up of thousands of genes containing very detailed information.

We learned about abnormalities of the number of chromosomes, about too little and too much genetic material, and we spent countless hours at the microscope, taking pictures and then cutting and pasting chromosomes to build karyotypes. These are maps of chromosomes used to count and analyze their shape, size, and appearance. I did not know at that time that genetics would have a profound effect on my life when several years later my first child was born with an incurable genetic abnormality. I also had no idea that many years later my youngest daughter would choose clinical genetics technology as her career.

Microbiology was a very pleasant surprise, but I think it had more to do with the teacher than the subject. I had the most amazing teacher; she was full of energy, and it was very contagious. She would get us excited about different kinds of bacteria and parasites and how they grew, developed, and adapted. She made what could have been a boring subject into a dynamic process of looking at the life of germs. To tell the truth, she was also single and very good looking, and I sort of had a crush on her and wanted to impress her. I studied hard and got a 100 in her class. Honestly, I don't think she ever noticed me.

She taught us how to set up cultures, count colonies, test antibiotics, and recognize each type of bacteria by its appearance in the cultures and its characteristics under the microscope. We also learned about parasites and how their lifecycles involved humans and animals. We studied how to identify them by looking at their eggs and their adult forms. For some of my classmates this was gross, for me it was stimulating!

Therapeutics is the branch of medicine that deals specifically with the treatment of disease and the art and science of healing. Even though this was a very broad subject, we mainly learned about the use of drugs and the method of their administration in the treatment of disease. It was something of a complement to pharmacology, but now we understood how drugs were administered and appreciated that treatments do not work equally for all people. To me the message was that medicine is a true art, and there are no absolutes; each treatment should be designed to fit the person, not just the disease.

Finally, our group got to go to our four-week course on Introduction to Clinical Medicine. I was so excited I was going to finally work with a patient, I could not wait to get started. My only fear was that I would be assigned to my father's course. Fortunately, I was assigned to Dr. Andrés's course. We met with him at the IMSS Centro Medico Nacional. This was one of the largest medical facilities in Mexico City. Dr. Andrés was the chief of service in one of the hospitals and had a reputation of being very demanding. We were told to meet in one of the conference rooms and bring our diagnostic tools, which in those days meant a stethoscope, a sphygmomanometer, and a light with an ophthalmoscope and otoscope attachments. I was so excited; I had had all these instruments ready for months, in a black leather bag all neatly packed. . .I was ready!

We arrived at the conference room; there were eight of us excited medical students. We had to wear white uniforms with a short white coat—this was required. Medical students were supposed to look like medical students! Dr. Andrés told us what he expected of us in the short four weeks we would be in his course. By the end of the four weeks, we were to be able to do a complete physical exam, know how to take a history, and organize our findings. I was not quite sure what he meant that day, but by the end of the course I had learned what would be the basis of my entire medical career.

The first two weeks, we did not get out of the classroom; we learned how to use our stethoscopes, how to listen, and where to use the stethoscope and how many other uses were there for it besides listening to the heart. We learned how valuable our ears could be in discerning where sounds were coming from and whether they were wet or dry; we listened to each other's hearts until we knew how normal hearts sounded like. Even though this was a tedious process, we would get excited when we were able to hear and identify a new sound.

We were also educated on how to measure blood pressure, how to determine the systolic (high) and the diastolic (low) components. I found it fascinating that blood pressure was not constant but an up-and-down pulse created by the heart. How magnificent was the human body, functioning with such dynamics while we are never aware of it. Sphygmomanometers, which have now been replaced by digital machines, were not just diagnostic tools, but a way to understand how things worked.

We looked into each other's ears and eyes and examined each other's mouths. Dr. Andrés taught us that there was a plethora of information hidden in each place. He also taught us to always be organized; it is easy to miss something when there is no methodological approach to an exam. We also examined each other's bodies; the two girls in the group were not very happy about it, but we were given limits and we all followed the rules. At the end of the first two weeks, we had a session with a male and female model the professor had hired. This time we were able to examine the whole human body, and with many giggles we made it through the session.

The third week was dedicated to how to take a medical history. Most importantly, we learned that taking a history has to be organized; you start with the present symptoms and move on to past history and then a review of each system. History was important and spending time doing it was crucial to making a diagnosis. Dr. Andrés emphasized this over and over again: never rush through the history! He told us that the patient needed to trust us, before he or she disclosed things that may be private and even embarrassing, so spending time to gain the patient's confidence was important. For Dr. Andrés, taking a history was more than just asking questions; it was about establishing a relationship with the patient. Probably one of the best pieces of advice I got in medical school.

The fourth week was here; we would actually meet and examined patients. Each one of us was given a patient every day, and we were to go to the patient's room, do a complete history and physical exam, and then in the afternoon we would present it to Dr. Andrés and the class.

My first patient was an eighty-nine-year-old man who was in the hospital because of abdominal pain. With much excitement and a little bit of fear, I went into the room and introduced myself. Mr. Carlos did not seem thrilled to see me; I was probably not the first medical student who had walked into his room. So I started my interrogation, which was going nowhere, until I remembered about establishing a rapport. Then I changed my tune and asked him about his family and what he had done with his life. Then he opened up and became very talkative. Little by little I obtained all the information I needed and did my physical exam. This was my first ever history and physical; it took me a little over three hours, but I came out of the room glowing!

In the afternoon presentations began; one by one we sat on a chair in front of the class and we presented our case, continuously being interrupted by Dr. Andrés. He wanted precise information! Hundreds of times I heard him say, "Don't guess!" Many were sent back to gather more information. "I don't know" was never the right answer. He never corrected anything without actually giving us an explanation; it was a somewhat embarrassing but very helpful exercise. These were his own patients, and he knew them well. One by one, all eight of us presented our cases, and by the time we were done it was eight o'clock at night, and we were tired. We all thought that we had done a great job, but it turned out that he did not agree. Fortunately, we could not wait to do a better job with our next patient.

The rest of the week went on the same way: new patient every morning and long discussions. Some days were hard, but with every mistake we made we learned a lesson. We also learned to be humble and realized that we did not know much. We helped and advised each other; by the end of the course we were a team, and we all helped to make sure we had all the information we needed to face Dr. Andrés. With each day we got better, the sessions got shorter, and by Friday we were able to go home by 6:00 p.m.

On Saturday, we met at the conference room, and Dr. Andrés told us that it was the end of his course and we did not have to see a patient. Then Dr. Andrés proceeded to tell us that he never gave individual grades but graded the class as a whole and was pleased to tell us that we all earned an MB (*muy bien*), which would translate as a 100. We all left energized and ready to take on our third year. We were so thankful to have met Dr. Andrés, one of many who would be responsible for our development. We had been introduced to clinical medicine, and we were ready to go forward!

What was going on in my life during these two years of medical school? Well, it was definitely not much. We spent many hours in the classroom every day and many afternoons and evenings studying. I was never a good night student; my friends would pull all-nighters frequently, especially during exams, but I found out I did not learn much after 8:00 p.m., so I would rather get up early and study before school.

I did manage to have a girlfriend. Tere, a beautiful, sweet girl; she had been my girlfriend since high school, and we remained together throughout medical school. I used to visit her at her home in the evenings, always under the watchful eye of her parents. We would sit in her living room and spend time talking and holding hands and sneaking a kiss every time we had a chance. We spent lots of time planning a future together that never happened.

On the weekends, we did get to go out sometimes, but always had to take with us her brother or sister as chaperone. Or if we were lucky we would double date with her older sister and her boyfriend, who happened to be my best friend Georges. Society in Mexico at that time was very traditional and strict. Our outings were either to the movies or friends' birthday parties, going out at night was rather expensive, and I did not have the means to pay for it.

Chapter 3
THE CLINICAL YEARS

The third year of medical school in Mexico is the start of what we call the clinical years. The next two years are spent at different hospital clinical departments. Medical students are assigned in small groups to a department and then given assignments within the services that each department provides. These hospitals are scattered throughout Mexico City and the surrounding area. It is the responsibility of the medical student to find transportation, and all students are required to wear white uniforms and short white coats as well as to carry their own diagnostic tools as explained in the previous chapter.

Most of the clinics were three- or six-week rotations and a few just two weeks. The medical students are part of the service teams, but they are at the bottom of the totem pole. Even though we got to take histories and do physical exams, we usually followed an intern and a resident; so most patients were not happy to see us walk into the room. During daily rounds we got to push a cart with a typewriter and type the daily notes as we went from patient to patient, for the attending physician or the resident to sign. Even though none of us ever had keyboard training (computers were not a part of life then), we all learned to type efficiently very quickly. These notes were placed in the patient record every day and chronicled the patient's progress; they were concise but comprehensive, and one could read these records years later and understand the patient's history. They may not have been innovative, but they were efficient.

We were all eager to learn to do procedures, but this was usually the job of the intern or the resident. Some were good teachers and enjoyed showing us, while others just wanted to get their job done. In some of the busier hospitals, medical students were much more involved as there was plenty to do. Even though these were the state or city hospitals that served the underprivileged, we all wanted to be assigned to them.

My first rotation was orthopedics. I was so happy! This was what I thought I wanted to do for the rest of my life. I was assigned to a large IMSS Medical Center. Our instructor was Dr. Fernando, a seasoned orthopedist who had been in practice for over twenty years. We enjoyed his rotation; each of us was assigned to follow an intern, and we got to see patients in the outpatient clinic and followed them up in the hospital if they needed surgery done. I got to observe many surgeries and scrubbed in as an assistant a few times. Even though I still liked orthopedics, I was a little disappointed on how much of it was like basic carpentry. I think the most important thing I learned during this rotation was surgical etiquette and surgical technic, which later on would become an important skill to have.

Then came gastroenterology, also at the same medical center. It just happened that the instructor, Dr. Luis, was a friend of my father. Even though I knew a lot already from just watching my father over the years, I found myself held to a higher standard than my classmates. If there was a question during rounds, I was always the first one to be asked, and my notes had to be retyped many times.

Even though both my father and grandfather were gastroenterologists, I was never attracted to the specialty. I found the fluoroscopic studies to be interesting, but dealing with some of the other unpleasant aspects of the intestinal tract never appealed to me. I was blessed with a very sensitive sense of smell, and it became a curse many times during my lifetime.

Then I had two short rotations: dermatology and forensic medicine. Dermatology was an easy one; we got assigned to a very busy outpatient dermatology clinic at a state hospital. Our instructor Dr. Maria Soledad was a fantastic teacher. We saw so many patients with her the first week, that the second week we were seeing patients by ourselves and making diagnosis and prescribing treatment on our own. We felt that we could recognize almost any skin disorder by the end of the rotation. I enjoyed it, but it was definitely not what I would have liked to do the rest of my life. Although, with no night call, no emergencies, or no weekend work, dermatology had definitely some appeal.

Needless to say, forensic medicine was not fun. On our first day, our instructor, a very stern and somber physician whose name I do not recall or maybe I do not want to recall, took us into the autopsy room and presented us with a body in an advanced state of decomposition. I could not bear the smell, so I went out and took an alcohol saturated cotton ball and stuffed it into my mask. As I returned to the room, it was obvious that the instructor noticed the wet spot on my mask, and from that day on, I was singled out for the worst jobs in the autopsies we helped with. I did not enjoy forensic medicine; I just quietly completed my assignments without a fuss. Unfortunately, I only made a 70, the lowest grade I had throughout my career.

Our second clinical semester turned out to be a very important one for me; the major rotations were pulmonology and cardiology; and otorhinolaryngology (ENT), hematology, ophthalmology, and nephrology were my short rotations.

I was assigned to take pulmonology at the Hospital para Enfermedades Pulmonares de Huipulco (Huipulco Respiratory Diseases Hospital), a state-owned old hospital originally established in 1936 for people with tuberculosis, which eventually became the internationally renowned National Institute of Respiratory Diseases. It was an old building, but well kept and clean through the years; but what was remarkable about this place was that it had a very advanced pulmonary function laboratory.

The hospital treated mostly adults and very few children. My patient assignments were mostly adults, but I started to like children more than adults, and I traded assignments with my friends every time I could. I became fascinated with how the lungs work and how to measure it and evaluate it. Dr. Rogelio, the head of the pulmonary function laboratory noticed it and took me under his wing. I also found out that I was good with children undergoing testing; I could get them to cooperate without a glitch.

At the end of six weeks I was ready to stay forever! I learned so much about the lungs, something that later on, when I went into neonatology, would become very important knowledge to have. I became persuaded that breathing was such an essential part of living that everybody should understand it to its fullest. Unfortunately I had to move on to my next rotation at the Instituto Nacional de Cardiología (Cardiology National Institute).

Like the pulmonary hospital this was a very large state-owned hospital. An old building, but staffed with a group of wonderful clinicians. At that point in time, cardiology had very few tools, physical exams, X-rays, and EKGs (electrocardiograms); ultrasound was just beginning to be used. I got to see one of the first rudimentary ultrasound machines being used; I always loved new gadgets! Ultrasound eventually became the most important advance in diagnostic cardiology since the discovery of X-rays. I felt I was at the cutting edge of technology!

My instructor was Dr. Ignacio; he was a wise old cardiologist, probably one of the best clinicians I ever met. For him, examining the heart not only involved listening but also observing the patient, taking the pulse, feeling the movement of the heart through the chest wall, and then using the stethoscope to listen. His lectures about the art of listening were fantastic. We learned to identify each and every sound in the normal cardiac cycle and to listen for anomalous sounds. You could tell so much about the heart just by listening; it was amazing.

We also spent countless hours learning about the normal electrical function of the heart and how to evaluate it with an EKG; each small peak, curve, or valley had significance, and once you understood this, it was easy to identify abnormalities. We literally looked at thousands of EKGs during the rotation. My friend's competitive spirit reemerged; we kept score every day on who got the right interpretation and then explained to each other the reasons. A healthy dose of competition was always a good thing to have.

I really enjoyed my cardiology rotation, and I found out again that I gravitated toward children. Every time I had the opportunity to trade an assignment and examine a child, I did. Dr. Ignacio was interested in applying this newfound ultrasound technology to infants and children with congenital heart defects, and I would volunteer to help him every time I could. The machine was a so-called M-Mode; it gave a continuous crosscut image of the heart, which you could see on a tiny orange screen. Sometimes he would print it on an old strip recorder and then measure the size of the chambers. His research was fascinating, and it started to pique my own interest in investigation.

The next four rotations ENT, hematology, ophthalmology, and nephrology were short two-week rotations. They were interesting, and I continued to learn more and more information, but besides being basic and necessary knowledge I had to acquire, they did not have a special meaning to me. I could have stayed in pulmonology and cardiology all semester! Although this may have had more to do with the wonderful instructors I had.

Oh boy! The third clinical semester was already here, and I knew it was going to be a hard one. Even though these were all short clinics, I dreaded the first two: neurology and psychiatry!

Having passed neuroanatomy in my first year, I knew how complex the nervous system was, and I was not looking forward to learning the diseases that affect it. But I was proven wrong again and was reminded once again of how a good teacher makes learning easier. Our instructor Dr. Miguel was an outstanding teacher and most of all a fabulous clinician. The first three days of our rotation was a boot camp on neurological examination. His most famous saying was "Anybody can tell that you are sick in the brain; it is finding out what part of the brain that is a challenge." We spent long hours learning about how to systematically explore the nervous system; his attention to detail was fantastic, and he did it in a way that was not only easy but, believe it or not, somewhat fun!

Neurological examination is somewhat different from that of other specialties in that you cannot examine the organ itself but what it does.

Each nerve has a function, and testing that function is where the answers are. The cognitive function or how we process thoughts, the senses of smell, hearing, and vision, eye movements, muscle strength, as well as reflexes and sensation all give clues as to brain's health. It is almost like detective work; the clues are there; you just have to find them.

Dr. Miguel's service was almost entirely in the outpatient clinic. We had daily lectures on neurological diseases and then we followed a resident around while he saw patients. It was a very busy clinic, so we got to do many examinations and saw many different kinds of patients. Each time we discussed our diagnosis with the resident, just to find out usually how little we knew. It was an eye-opening experience; it gave us a totally new perspective on the complexity of neurological disease. Unfortunately, many neurological disorders are not curable, while others can only be controlled; few diseases seemed to have a true cure. It is a very difficult specialty, and you need to be a special person to work in it. It was definitely not for me; things like strokes, dementia, Alzheimer's disease, Parkinson's, multiple sclerosis, and neuromuscular disease were very hard for me to see.

The hardest thing that I experienced during my neurology rotation was when Dr. Miguel was called into the hospital to make an assessment of brain-dead in a patient in the intensive care unit (ICU). This was a young man who had been in a car accident and had a severe head injury. After one week in a coma, there were no signs of recovery. He did a very careful examination with many specialized tests that check for any reaction to pain, light, or heat. Then a careful EEG (electroencephalogram) was done, which showed no electrical evidence of brain activity. He also reviewed the record to make sure the patient was not on any medications that would interfere with the tests. Then he called the family to the chapel and in very simple terms explained to them that there was no hope that the patient would recover. He held the wife's hand while he talked in a very soft but firm voice. He told them they had a choice, but his recommendation was to terminate life support. They agreed; we all sat in silence for a few minutes and then Dr. Miguel hugged the wife and his parents, and we all left the room. I went home and cried; it was a sad but humbling experience, and I had seen a totally different side of Dr. Miguel that I will never forget.

On Fridays, we had two hours where we looked at CT scans (no MRIs back then), and Dr. Miguel, along with the radiologist, would go over them with us, and discuss what to look for in different disorders, and we would look at EEGs, which I'll have to say, I never understood, and even to this day look like a bunch of squiggly lines on paper to me. Again, it takes a special person to go through these records and make sense out of them. I was definitely not one of them.

Our next rotation was at the Hospital Psiquiátrico Fray Bernardino Alvarez, a psychiatric hospital on the outskirts of Mexico City, with a very interesting history. This hospital was inaugurated three years earlier and was built to replace the Manicomio (madhouse) General La Castañeda. La Castañeda had been built in 1910 to house mental patients because most of them were stripped and abandoned by their families. There was a time when the hospital lodged more than three thousand inpatients, three times its capacity. La Castañeda had a reputation for injustice and mistreatment of inmates. It was a sad period in the history of psychiatry in Mexico. Inmates were not considered curable; hypnosis, hydrotherapy, pain, and electroshock were the only treatments offered. In the 1960s, an investigation, which would earn the name Operación Castañeda, culminated in the dismantling of the asylum.

My mother used to tell me every time I acted up that I was going to be taken to La Castañeda!

With this background in mind, I started my rotation at Fray Bernardino. We were certainly afraid of going into this institution that had secured entrance doors. I think we were still expecting to walk into the madhouse. Our instructor, Dr. Ramon, was a very well respected psychiatrist. He was part of a new generation of physicians who believed that investigation into mental illness was as important as in any other field. We had lectures every day, and we saw patients in the classroom. We were never allowed to roam the wards as in other hospitals, and what we thought would be a difficult rotation went on fast. We got a relatively superficial look at the specialty, but I had all I needed for the rest of my career.

During the third semester we also had two elective courses to take; I picked History of Medicine and Endocrinology. Endocrinology was particularly interesting to me because during my high-school years I had lost about forty pounds, inexplicably over a short period of time as well as becoming tremulous and restless. I was so thin that my mother used to call me Don Quixote. Eventually I was diagnosed with Grave's disease or hyperthyroidism; my thyroid gland had gone crazy and was producing more thyroid hormone than I needed. I was placed on thyroid suppression drugs, and in a few months I had regained all my weight and was back to normal. I was hoping to find some answers to why it had happened.

Our course was at one of the specialty hospitals of the IMSS, and we had a very charismatic instructor. Her main interests were diabetes and thyroid disease, so she was perfect! Her name was Dr. Ana Marta, and she was a good teacher, but very detailed; she wanted us to learn every single substance involved in the production of hormones and every pathway they took to convey their effect. As usual my memory skills served me well, and I did well in her course, but I did not find the answers I was looking for. Eventually, when I went through my residency, this information became very valuable, and I will always be thankful for Dr. Ana Marta's attention to minutiae.

I have always been very fond of history, so the History of Medicine elective was an easy choice. Besides, it was taught at the Old Medical School building downtown Mexico City. This was the building where my grandfather and my father studied medicine. The original building had been built in 1736, and was the headquarters of the Spanish Inquisition until 1820 when it became the home of the medical school. In its courtrooms, many people were persecuted and found guilty of heresy and witchcraft and sentenced to life imprisonment or, in some cases, to die at the stake or be hanged. Currently, it houses the Museum of Mexican Medicine, its historical archives and a library as well as the Department of History and Philosophy of the School of Medicine of the UNAM.

The building is a beautiful baroque building with the traditional courtyard surrounded by columns that end on suspended arches. Walking in the courtyard gave you a feeling of pride; it was exciting. I was at the place my grandfather and father had studied medicine, and we were in the same classrooms, sitting in the same chairs! Our instructor was Dr. Felipe, a full professor in UNAM, and an incredible source of information. We had daily lectures from him and his staff; even though we had to spend hours in the bus to get downtown, it was worth it. The history of world and Mexican medicine was a fascinating topic. From ancient Greece to the Aztecs, from the Spanish conquistadores to generations of great Mexican doctors, I enjoyed every minute of it.

We were now entering our fourth and last clinical semester. I was looking forward to the last long rotations: obstetrics and gynecology, and pediatrics. The last short ones were urology, sports medicine, and infectious diseases; even though they sounded interesting I just wanted to get them over!

My obstetrics and gynecology rotation was at the Maternidad Isidro Espinosa de los Reyes, a very busy state-owned institution. It was only about a five-minute drive from home, so it was a welcome change from having to drive through Mexico City's busy traffic, and the gossip was that students got a lot of hands-on experience. With an average of six thousand deliveries a year they needed help. This maternity hospital eventually became the Instituto Nacional de Perinatología (INPer), which is now a well-known institute in perinatal research.

Our instructor Dr. Armando met us in a classroom and explained to us that we would spend most of our rotation in the obstetrics department, and we would also attend the gynecology clinic at the Hospital de la Mujer, which just happened to be on the other side of the city. Fortunately, this would only be a week of the entire rotation. Initially, we had several lectures on obstetrics: pregnancy, labor, and delivery. The first week we were allowed to follow a resident or an intern as he or she attended to women in labor and deliveries, and in the afternoon we would make rounds in the ward. By the second week we were helping the residents as they attended deliveries and observing C-sections, and by the third week we were following women in labor and attending deliveries by ourselves and then doing rounds on them in the afternoons, and with the blessing of the resident discharging them home along with their babies.

The hospital was a very poor hospital; supplies were scarce, and the nurses were very obsessive about us not wasting anything. We were allowed one pair of gloves daily; between vaginal exams or deliveries we would wash them with soap and water and go on to the next patient. The only time we could get a second pair was if the gloves tore. But I found myself actually delivering a few babies with my bare hands. Disposable plastic syringes were recycled and gas sterilized multiple times, and so were needles. The nurses would even sharpened old needles to make them last.

My introduction to obstetrics was quite dramatic; on my second day, as I was walking in the hospital, I heard a woman yelling as she walked through the front door, "My baby is coming!" I ran to help her, and as I approached her she lifted her dress and there it was, the baby's head was out and the rest was definitely coming. I grabbed the head with my hands, her husband helped her lie back, and the baby continued to come until I found myself holding a brand new baby, still attached to his umbilical cord, and crying in my arms! I was in shock initially, but as the hospital staff arrived and wrapped the baby on a blanket, a nurse handed me a pair of forceps and scissors and directed me to cut the cord. Wow! I could not believe I had just delivered my first baby! Nobody could wipe the grin off my face that day.

There was only one labor ward where all women without problems would come to labor; unfortunately, it had only eight beds. We would send patients to labor outside in the lobby, where they walked back and forth until they were dilated enough that delivery was imminent or they felt an urge to push. We eventually named the lobby La Sala de los Dolores (the pains hall). Periodically, we would bring our patients to be examined and take them to the delivery room if they were ready. We kept track of each patient, and if she did not seem to be making normal progress, we would call the resident for advice; otherwise, we would attend the delivery, resuscitate the baby, and perform any repairing that was needed. Then we would send mother and baby happily to their room. There was no anesthesia unless the patient required a procedure like a forceps extraction or a C-section. I was always amazed at how well women did and how short labor was. Later on in life I realized that having women labor in bed and giving epidurals may not be in their best interests.

Many of our patients were indigenous Mexican Indians, and, occasionally, their language and their different culture was a problem. Many were delivering their second or third baby. Their previous babies had been delivered at home by a *partera* (midwife). We were at a disadvantage; as far as they were concerned we knew nothing! I will never forget the time when one of these women was ready to deliver and when I asked her to climb onto the delivery table she refused. She had delivered her previous children squatting, and that was what she was going to do. Eventually, we compromised, and she got up on the table squatted and delivered the baby her way!

Even though all this may appear to be grossly inadequate care, the C-section rate was only 4.5 percent, and the majority of babies had no problems and were breastfeeding immediately after delivery and went home by the third day without complications. Maybe there is a lesson here that we should consider revisiting sometime.

I absolutely loved my five weeks in obstetrics; it was a lot of fun! I delivered fifteen babies by myself and enjoyed every minute in the delivery room. The anticipation and excitement of a new life being born is something I always liked throughout my career and the one I miss the most.

I learned a lot by just being there; these women and their newborns taught me lessons I would never forget. If anything, I learned that babies are born with, without, and sometimes in spite of the doctors. Just as my father used to say!

Gynecology was not as exciting; we spent most of our week in the outpatient clinic seeing patients with our instructor, and we got to attend a few surgical procedures. Even though it was interesting, and I always enjoyed helping in surgery, this was definitely not my cup of tea.

We moved on to our short clinics: urology, sports medicine, and infectious diseases. Urology was interesting, but it seemed to be a little like plumbing. Following the flow of urine through tubes and investigating obstructions was challenging, but the tools for exploring were very few: a good physical exam, X-rays, and fluoroscopy with contrast. Back then there were no scopes or lithotripsy, so besides drugs to relax the ureters, antibiotics, or surgery, treatments were not very effective. It seemed like every patient either had kidney stones, an infection, or cancer. We also saw male patients with problems in their reproductive organs. Venereal disease, prostate problems, and testicular cancer seemed to be the most common. Occasionally, we would see an infertility patient referred for evaluation; it was somewhat fun to do sperm counts under the microscope. Female reproductive problems were seen by the gynecologists, so the majority of the urology clinic patients were male.

Next was sports medicine; it was at one of the largest IMSS orthopedic hospitals, and our instructor was Dr. Victorio, whom I knew very well. He had operated on my leg after a soccer injury four years earlier, and he also happened to be the father of one of my best friends in high school. He was a superb teacher, and he surrounded himself with many bright young orthopedists who were in charge of most of the lectures. Sports medicine was a very new field; most of the injuries we saw were severe, and surgeries were very involved. Injuries to the knee and ankle were usually career ending for many athletes.

Mexico had just hosted the 1968 Olympics, and the term *sports medicine* had just been coined in 1961. The field was on the upswing. Dr. Victorio was a pioneer; he had brought to Mexico new and exciting techniques and procedures that were just being tested. The Watanabe arthroscope had just been demonstrated by Dr. Robert Jackson in Toronto, and Dr. Victorio had just come back from one of the first major educational courses on arthroscopy. He was gearing up to start using the new procedure in Mexico. He was such an innovator; eventually, one of the largest orthopedic hospitals of the IMSS was named after him.

We learned a lot from him and his staff, but most of all we learned what sets sports medicine apart from other areas of medicine. Sports medicine physicians are proactive in regard to the treatment options for athletes. Sports medicine physicians don't like to wait until an injury occurs, but they aim to continuously minimize risk in athletes to achieve best results.

The last short rotation was coming: infectious diseases. We were sent to the Hospital de Infectología del Centro Médico Nacional La Raza, a large hospital in the north of the city. It was a relatively old hospital opened in 1954, but it had the reputation for being one of the premier referral centers for infectious disease. The rumor was that it was the best place to learn. It was also the only IMSS unit approved for infectious disease training.

Dr. Daniel was our instructor; he was a seasoned physician and researcher, with an outstanding reputation as a teacher. On our first meeting he told us that we would attend daily afternoon lectures, which would be given, most of the time, by his residents and staff, and we would spend the mornings one week in the outpatient clinic and the other in the microbiology laboratory. That was the last time we saw him; the rest of the rotation was all handled by his staff. We were somewhat disappointed, but it turned out that he had put together a very bright group of people; actually, we never missed him.

The lectures were excellent, very practical in terms of diagnosis, treatment, and prevention of infections. We covered laboratory tests and cultures, antibiotics and vaccines; there was so much to learn! For me though, the best part of the rotation and what would become more helpful in the future was the microbiology laboratory. Here we learned how to handle specimens, how to set up cultures, and how to read them after they have been incubated. We would be assigned to a technologist who would teach us individually. I will forever be thankful for Señorita Margarita, who put up with me for five days, answered all my questions, and never stopped smiling.

The outpatient clinic was totally different; we got to see many patients with a variety of infectious diseases. Unfortunately, although they were getting appropriately treated, many would go back home to live in the same unsanitary conditions that gave them the problem to begin with. The scope of practice in the clinic went beyond medicine; most of these diseases were related to poverty. Social workers and nurse educators were as important or more than the doctors. Things like intestinal amebiasis and parasites were very common. In Mexico diarrhea and dehydration was one of the most common causes of infant mortality.

I had a hard time seeing children coming in with parasites and being treated for it. We knew they would go home and get infested again. Most of them were filthy, and their mothers did not know any better. They lived in houses with dirt floors and no running water. I wanted to take them home with me and clean them up, but I knew that it would not change anything. Our week in the outpatient clinic gave me very mixed feelings; this was a sad part of medicine that I was not ready for.

It was the end of our infectious disease rotation, and we knew that we had only one more rotation to go and then we would be ready to go into our rotating internships. Manuel, Juan, Enrique, and I had our sights on obtaining an internship in the Unites States. My brother, several years earlier, had done his in Mt. Vernon, NY, and he loved it. So we had researched hospitals that took foreign medical students and had started sending applications. We even hired an English teacher to prepare us. I was comfortable with the language, but I felt a refresher would not hurt.

My whole life revolved around finding out where I was going to do my internship. With one rotation to go, I had a grade average of 93. I knew I could get an internship in Mexico without a problem, but I was hoping that I would hear from a hospital in the United States. I really wanted to follow in my brother's footsteps; he had really enjoyed his internship. He even found his wife during that time!

Life was no different during the final clinical year; I used to study every evening while my mother watched her soap operas. I found out that I could learn things better when there was background noise; soap operas were ideal. Although, I must admit, sometimes I would get wrapped up in the plot and come back the next evening just to find out what happened. My mother enjoyed the company anyway.

I still called on Tere any time I could and found time to party a little or go out to the movies occasionally. I would get together with my friends from high school, and we would go at night to *llevar gallo* (serenade) our girlfriends. This was not unusual; we would practice several songs and would sing under all our girlfriends' windows! Sometimes, knowing how to play the guitar and having a decent voice was handy, and it did not cost any money! I loved Tere, but there was so much going on in my life that I did not have much time to think much about our relationship; we were young, things were happening, and I was sure that all would work out for the best.

The year was 1971, and I was entering my last rotation: pediatrics. I had no idea at that time that eventually I would be in love with the specialty and spend the rest of my life taking care of children.

We started our rotation at the Hospital Infantil de México another institution with an interesting history. Since 1933, a group of members of the Sociedad Mexicana de Pediatría (Mexican Pediatric Society) had been pushing for an institution dedicated to children only. Planning went on for the next ten years, and, finally, on April 30, 1943, the first pediatric hospital in Mexico was inaugurated. It was a very modern and beautiful building equipped with the latest technology. For the next fourteen years, it was considered the most prestigious pediatric hospital in Mexico, Central, and South America. Unfortunately, on July 28, 1957, at 2:00 a.m., Mexico City suffered a devastating earthquake, which seriously affected the structure of the hospital. Continuing work at this facility was considered too risky, so all patients and equipment were moved next door to the Maternidad (maternity) Mundet building, while demolition and rebuilding was done. Regrettably, it took over thirty-seven years, until 1994, for the current modern Hospital Infantil to be built and open its doors.

My rotation was at the Maternidad Mundet. The hospital was a very busy one; most beds were usually full, and each bed was usually surrounded by a family, sometimes rather large. We started every morning at 7:00 a.m. We would check on the sickest patients and review their condition in the clinical record. At 8:00 a.m., rounds started with a large team of people, usually the head of department or the attending physician, accompanied by the residents and the head nurse. We usually followed with the typewriter and updated the notes as we went from patient to patient. This was my first exposure to teamwork; the bedside nurses participated in the discussion just as much as the residents. It was amazing to watch them discuss each patient, make a plan for the day, and update the family, all in a wonderfully organized way. Even our notes were neatly organized as the resident dictated them to us; our typing skills were really put to the test, but we seemed to manage to get things done on time.

When rounds were over, we had a short break to grab something to eat and then we continued to the academic sessions where one patient was presented by a first-year resident and the disease and treatment discussed by the group. We were allowed to participate in the discussion, and it turned out to be the best learning experience we had in all the rotations. In the afternoon, we returned to the floors to recheck on all our critical patients, and when everybody was done with their work, we concluded the day with the change of the guard when the residents would hand over to the night staff, informing them about any special needs their patients had. It was interesting to me that there was no specific time to check out, but the rule was that all procedures, notes, and updates to the families had to be done before anybody could go home. Some of us students would stay late and follow the resident on call, but since there was no place for us to sleep, usually by ten o'clock we would go home and then start all over at 7:00 a.m. We worked hard, learned a lot, and slept little. But it was a fun rotation.

I became captivated by the children; I was always able to go to their bedsides and talk to them and get them to talk to me. It was very rewarding to see them and their families go home, but it was also very sad to see those who did not make it. I did find out that I had a hard time not getting emotionally involved, but in spite of the warnings from the residents and attending physicians, I did. On many occasions I even visited my discharged patients at home. Only one thing bothered me: that a lot of newborns who were admitted or transferred from other hospitals did not do well, especially those who were premature; there were not many therapies that could be offered. It seemed that we just put them on oxygen and then watched them die.

I would go home and talk to my father about it, and he would always tell me that we had limitations, and these babies were better off not being saved. In some way he was right; some of the few survivors faced a life with severe disabilities; death was not such a terrible alternative, and the families seemed to accept it better than I could. I did not know then that I would spend a large part of my life taking care of these babies and proving that they could not only be saved but grow up to be normal.

We were almost at the end of our last rotation, and none of us had a position for an internship anywhere. We had sent applications to twelve hospitals in the United States and Canada, and so far we had heard only from two and both were negative. We would be finished with pediatrics in August, and in Mexico most internship programs started January 1, so we felt comfortable as we still had time, but we were getting a little nervous; if we waited too long we may not find a place anywhere.

And then it happened! We were all meeting for our English lesson, and as we walked in we were all carrying a letter in our hands. All five of us had received the same letter from a hospital in Massachusetts. It read that they had two rotating internship positions open from November 1 if we were interested, but they wanted us to choose who would go since all our CVs were comparable. Immediately Manuel and Miguel said they were willing to give up their spots; both had families with connections and had already lined up internships. It was up to Enrique, Juan, and me to decide. We decided to flip a coin each and two heads or tails would go. Don Miguel, the English professor, would be the judge.

We were all nervous; we flipped: heads, heads, and. . .heads! It was nerve racking! So we flipped again. Enrique uncovered his coin: heads. Then Juan removed his hand: tails. It was up to me to decide who was going. Reluctantly, I moved my hand: heads! It would be Enrique and I who would take the positions. Framingham Union Hospital would be our next big adventure. We were both ecstatic; Juan on the contrary was sad to miss the opportunity, but he was a good sport and said nothing. Who could have known at this point that he would eventually come to the United States for residency training and become a very well-known perinatologist in Dallas, Texas.

We got busy sending our papers and arranging our passports while we finished our pediatric rotation. We received our *cartas de pasante* (graduate letter), a sort of permit to practice medicine under supervision in August. We had a big graduation party with all the remaining students who had started as group 601. From the original forty-one students, only twelve of us received our letters. All my family was there, and my beloved Tere was at my side. We felt like we were on top of the world; finishing medical school was a great accomplishment. We were ready to take on the world!

Chapter 4
FIRST EXPERIENCE AND INTERNSHIP

After our graduation, we all became *pasantes*, probably the equivalent of "graduates." We were allowed to practice but under supervision. Technically, our next step would be our internship, but since Enrique and I had a couple of months until the start of our internship in Framingham, I decided to try to do something to make some money to take on the trip.

I found a job staffing a small office in a town just outside Mexico City. It was a general practice office located in the same building as a pharmacy. The office and the pharmacy were owned by a doctor. I met with him, and he told me the deal was that I would practice under his supervision at the office at no charge. I would be allowed to collect fee for service from all the patients I treated and keep 100 percent of the proceeds. The only catch was that I would be at the office at least six hours every day but Sunday, and I would recommend that all medications I prescribed be filled in at the pharmacy next door. That seemed like a good deal to me; I even got to pick my own hours and set my own fees.

The town was called San Pedro Cuajimalpa, a small town of about ten thousand people located just outside Mexico City. It was about a fifteen-minute car ride from home. My first day there was September 6, 1972, a date I will never forget, especially since two years later it would become my wedding date. I arrived at eight o'clock in the morning. I was excited, dressed in a tie and a clean white coat. I was carrying my black leather bag with all my diagnostic equipment and even a prescription pad with my name, which I had gotten as a present for graduation.

I opened the office to find that it was just a single room, with a desk, three chairs, an examining table, and a sink. There was no bathroom! I went next door and talked to the pharmacist, who explained to me that I was welcome to use their bathroom as previous doctors had done. As I returned to my office, there was a middle-aged woman waiting for me outside the door. I asked her to give me a minute to set my things and I would see her. I went back inside, pulled all my shiny instruments out, and full of excitement I asked my very first patient to come in.

Her name was Consuelo (it translates as comfort), a name I will never forget; she was forty years old and a typical native Mexican Indian. I started to do my history, and she proceeded to tell me everything about herself, her children, and her husband, a lot more than I needed to know. I did my exam, which turned out to be somewhat limited since she would not remove any of her garments. I found out this to be very common when dealing with Indian women. I had to listen to their hearts and lungs and examine their abdomens through their clothes. Eventually, I came to the conclusion that her problem was gastritis from drinking *pulque*, an alcoholic drink made from agave. I advised her to stop drinking and gave her the prescriptions for the appropriate medications. She then asked me how much she owed me. I was not prepared for that! I was about to panic when she told me that the previous doctor used to charge fifteen pesos for the consultation. I breathed a sigh of relief and told her that was right. She paid me cash, and as she left, I thought to myself, I had just had my first patient and my first fees. I was a real doctor! What a great day!

As she left I went back into my office to wash my hands; I realized I had nothing but water. So I went next door to the pharmacy and bought a bar of soap, and the pharmacist suggested I may also want to buy some paper towels, cotton balls, alcohol, and a few other things he thought I would need. I left the pharmacy with supplies that cost me more than the fifteen pesos I had just earned.

The rest of the day went on very slowly; in my six hours I saw two more patients, both with simple problems. By two o'clock, I closed and locked the office and left. When I arrived at home, my mother was waiting for me, eager to listen to my new adventure. Even though I was a little disappointed with my three patients, I shared my story and she, as always, was very encouraging and advised me to be patient; word of mouth was very powerful and my practice would pick up soon.

Wow! She was right; my second day was a busy one. The word was out that there was a new doctor, and I had patients waiting outside the office all day. On my second day, I saw fifteen patients! Mostly simple things, but a couple of children had unusual rashes that the mothers called *sarna*, which when I looked up my book turned out to be scabies. I sure knew how to treat that! Unfortunately, when I suggested that the whole family had to shampoo I met a lot of opposition; I had to spend a lot of time explaining. They seemed to like that I spent time explaining why and seemed to leave the office satisfied with their prescription.

I made a whopping $215pesos! Not quite what it should have been, but two patients explained to me that if they paid me the fifteen pesos they would not have enough money to pay for the prescription, so I settled for ten pesos. It actually gave me a sense of satisfaction to be able to help those who could not afford the fifteen pesos. By the time I went home, it was almost 4:00 p.m., and my mother greeted me with a big smile on her face that seemed to say, "I told you so." I was very excited; not only did I love what I was doing, but for the first time, I also got paid for it.

That evening I called Tere and invited her to dinner to celebrate my achievement. It was nice to have somebody to share my experience with. We also talked about my upcoming internship. I would be gone for a year, and we made promises to stay in touch by writing letters, and maybe the occasional phone call. It was very sad to think that we would not see each other for a year, but we were sure we were up to the challenge.

My eight-week adventure was full of surprises; I had a variety of challenging patients. The majority were very humble Mexican Indians, but all of them treated me with utmost respect. I felt that they would do exactly as

I said. Being a doctor seemed to carry a responsibility I never appreciated before. I felt I had a duty to do my best. Many times, if I was not sure of what to do, I would ask them to come the next day for free, while I consulted with my father or my friends. They appreciated my honesty.

One day a small child walked into the office with his mother, covered in blood. He had fallen and hit his head and had a pretty good-size laceration on the scalp. I cleaned it up, and I knew he needed stiches. I had my instruments and a way to boil them to sterilize them, but I was missing xylocaine and suture material. I went next door and asked my friendly pharmacist, and he told me to just write the prescription and send the mother over and he would send me what I needed and he sure did. That was the first time I sutured somebody by myself, but I was satisfied with the results and sent him on his way. I instructed him to come back in a week to get the stitches removed; he never returned. I found out later that his father removed the stitches with a knife.

It was not unusual to prescribe an injection, most of the time antibiotics. Long-acting penicillin was the treatment of choice for strep throat. So I would give the patients the prescription for the penicillin and a disposable syringe, and they would return for me to give them the shot. I usually charged three pesos for injecting. I remember one patient very well, a very sick teenage girl who had the most swollen ugly looking tonsils I have ever seen, and she was also febrile. I was sure this was strep; so I gave her the prescription and told her to go fill it up next door. She looked at me with teary eyes and told me she did not have enough money. She expressed that all she had was five pesos and she was hoping I would take them for the consultation, but she could not afford the medicine. I could not help it, I reached into my pocket and handed her a twenty-peso bill and told her to go get everything. I will never forget her expression; she got up, hugged me, and ran out of the office. For a minute I thought I might not see her again, but she was back in a few minutes, with the medicine, the syringe, and my change. I gave her the shot and sent her on her way. Then I sat at my desk and pondered: What just did happen?"

I have great memories of my first interaction with patients during my two months in San Pedro Cuajimalpa. I did not make a lot of money, but

I saved enough to have a little cash for my trip. I was able to make a repu-tation for myself and left with the undying love and appreciation of the community.

Most importantly, I gained invaluable experience; I had set up my own charges, which I thought were realistic and fair, but I had the freedom to adjust them as I saw fit, depending on the patient's ability to pay. Nobody told me what I should charge, nor did anybody tell me what discounts I could and could not make. It was all between my patient and me; unfortu-nately, that was the last time I would be able to have that freedom.

San Pedro Cuajimalpa, forty years later, has been fully incorporated into the urban sprawl of Mexico City. Its population has grown to over 180,000 people. Much of the territory has been urbanized and contains some of the city's most expensive residential and commercial real estate, with newer developments for upper classes pushing out lower income groups. The former rural town is still there, even though only very few of the old traditional houses remain; the historic center of the town and the pharmacy still exist.

November was here! It was time to leave for Framingham Union Hospital. My family and Enrique's took us to the airport. His girlfriend Blanca and Tere were also there. We hugged and cried, and I kissed Tere good-bye in front of my parents, something I had never done before. I guess it was OK since I did not get the evil eye from my mother. Enrique and I boarded the plane; there was a feeling of excitement and a little fear in both of us, but we made an effort not to show it.

We were to travel from Mexico City to Boston, and Dr. Cesare, the head of education at Framingham, had arranged for a van to pick us up at the airport and drive us to Framingham. It was an all-day trip; we had a two-hour layover in Dallas, and we would be arriving at Logan International Airport in Boston at 5:00 p.m. Framingham was only twenty-five miles away, so we figured we would arrive at the hospital by dinnertime.

It all went without a glitch; as we arrived in Boston, we found the driver of the van holding a sign with our last names. We picked up our luggage, and off we went. Unfortunately, we did not know about rush hour. The supposedly thirty-minute ride to Framingham turned into a two-hour traffic nightmare. We finally arrived at the hospital at eight o'clock; the driver unloaded our luggage and left us at the hospital's main entrance. We had no idea where to go.

We went in, and as soon as the lady at the information desk saw us she came running. She knew who we were and was expecting us. She walked us to the living quarters next to the hospital. It was a three-story old house, with lots of rooms where the interns and residents lived or stayed while on duty. She showed us to our room on the second floor. It was small; it had two beds, two desks, two dressers with drawers, and a small closet. We were so tired and hungry; all we wanted to do was have a bite to eat and get some rest. The information desk lady, Mrs. Virginia, was very nice to us and told us how to get to the cafeteria but warned us that it would not be open till midnight for the eleven to three shift's breakfast but that there were vending machines where we could purchase a snack in the meantime.

We quickly decided which bed would be whose. I liked the one close to the window and Enrique liked the other one, so there was no problem. We put our luggage down and proceeded to the cafeteria. There were only two vending machines, so we loaded up on Twinkies, Bear Paws, and a Coke and headed up back to our room. After "dinner" we put on our pajamas and went right to sleep without even giving a thought to setting an alarm clock or what the next day would bring. We were there, and that was all that mattered.

The next morning we woke up at what we thought was 8:00 a.m., cleaned up and dressed in our bright white uniforms, and headed to the hospital to find the office. When we arrived there we realized it was almost 10:00 a.m.! We were on eastern time; something we had not taken into account. Dr. Cesare turned out to be the sweetest Italian man; he was about seventy years old, and he had just retired as chief of pathology to become director of education. He welcomed us and told us we would start working under the category of "externs" for the first few weeks, while we were introduced to all the hospital departments and policies. We would take no call till a time he decided we were ready. We did not quite know what he meant; obviously, we felt we were ready already!

Then he took us to the cardiac ICU, where he introduced us to Dr. Frank, who was in charge of the internal medicine program; he was also in charge of the house staff who rotated through the service from Boston City Hospital. Most of them were second- and third-year residents. This unit was the pride of Framingham. The hospital had participated in the Framingham Heart Study since 1948. Under the direction of the National Heart Institute, the Framingham Heart Study was to identify the common factors or characteristics that contribute to cardiovascular disease. Over five thousand men and women between the ages of thirty and sixty-two from the town of Framingham were recruited and followed with extensive physical examinations and lifestyle interviews.

In 1971, one year before we arrived, the study had enrolled a second generation and was an ongoing project. Over the years, monitoring of the Framingham population had led to the identification of the major cardio-vascular disease risk factors—high blood pressure, high blood cholesterol, smoking, obesity, diabetes, and physical inactivity. It was exciting to learn that we would be part of such a fantastic study.

After that, Dr. Cesare introduced us to the obstetrics labor and deliv-ery nurses, and we met a couple of obstetricians: Dr. Paul and Dr. Joseph. Both of them seemed very personable and made us feel welcome. Then we went to the pediatric ward, where we were introduced to the most dynamic group of nurses I have ever worked with. Finally, we went up to the surgical floor and met the surgical staff; everybody seemed excited about having a couple of Mexicans on the staff.

After the grand tour, Dr. Cesare took us to the cafeteria, where he explained to us that the service was buffet style, and we were allowed to eat all we wanted during our stay. Meals were free for all working interns, and we could also have our meals there on our days off. This was fantastic; the food was good, and we would not have to worry about where to eat our meals.

During lunch we met the other interns who had been there since July. They were Dr. Rakesh from India, Dr. Shigeru from Japan, Dr. Marco from Argentina, Dr. Kim from Korea, and Dr. Christine, the only

American in the group. Apparently, we were the first Mexicans ever to work at the hospital. I believe that was the reason why they were cautious about letting us loose right away. We had something to prove!

After lunch we went to the emergency room (ER), met the staff, and also met Dr. Jeremiah, a local surgeon, who was there suturing a laceration. He shook our hands and said, "Welcome to the pit." I had never worked in an ER before, but it looked like a stimulating place to work. The head nurse, Ms. Judy, showed us around and gave us a piece of advice that would become very valuable in the future: "When in doubt. . .ask a nurse; chances are she has been working here a lot longer than you."

We went back to Dr. Cesare's office, where he explained that we would be paid $240 a month, and our housing and meals would always be free. It seemed like a lot of money; if translated into pesos it was $3,000 a month—a fortune! We gave him our documents and signed some forms and then he told us to go back to our rooms, unpack, and get settled. Dinner was served from 6:00 to 8:00 p.m. at the cafeteria. He expected us at eight o'clock in the morning in his office ready to start working.

Enrique and I went back to our room; it was time to explore a little. The house had three levels. The upper two levels were rooms. The third floor belonged to the residents from Boston and the middle floor to the Framingham interns. There were seven of us, but even though we all had rooms assigned, only Dr. Rakesh, Dr. Kim, and we were living there. Dr. Shigeru and Dr. Marco were married and were living in apartments close to the hospital with their wives. Dr. Chris who was also married, owned a house with her husband a few miles away. The only nights they slept at the house was when they were on call.

The first floor had a small lounge that had several sofas and a TV. There was also a small kitchen that we could use and a refrigerator that we found out was fair game to all, so nothing was safe there. The back door opened to a small yard with a sitting area that overlooked what we thought was a lake, although we were corrected many times that it was only a pond. In November, when we arrived, it was rather cold for us warm-blooded Mexicans, so we did not spend much time outside.

The next morning we were up bright and early, had breakfast at the cafeteria, with the other interns, and went to see Dr. Cesare. He assigned Enrique to pair up with Shigeru in the surgical service, and I was paired with Dr. Chris in internal medicine. The first thing she told me was that we really did not do much in the cardiac ICU since it was run by the Boston residents, but we were in charge of working up any admission to the service. She suggested that I review a couple of charts so that I could get an idea of how we were asked to do the histories.

That was my first shock! I picked up a chart, and it read,

"This is a 56 y/o WF with known COPD adm for tx bc of RD possibly 2' to CHF bc of a ↓ PCV."

I had no idea what I had just read, so I asked Dr. Chris if she would translate it for me, she read,

"This is a 56-year-old white female admitted for transfusion because of Respiratory Distress probably secondary to Congestive Heart Failure because of a low Packed Cell Volume."

Some things I could have guessed, but I knew right there I had a lot to learn. My first two days following Dr. Chris I spent writing initials and abbreviations in a notebook and asking her to translate them to me. By the third day, I could handle most of the code, but this was such a change from our notes in Mexico. We were always required to write every word and be grammatically correct. This was certainly not the case here.

After the first week, I felt very confident that I could do what Dr. Chris was doing, and Enrique felt the same way with Dr. Shigeru. We told Dr. Cesare, but he told us to be patient for another week. He explained to us that most of the patients at Framingham were private patients. When a physician in the community decided a patient was to be admitted to the hospital, he would arrange the admission, the admitting office would notify the intern, and the intern was responsible for admitting the patient, doing the history and physical exam, and deciding along with the admitting physician what the plan would be. He asked us to be patient and just follow our comrades. He would make sure that they would give us more free rein the second week.

On Monday of the second week, Chris told me, "The next admission is yours; I will be here if you need me." I was so excited; I think I called the admitting office myself several times. Finally, almost at the end of my shift, I got the phone call. Dr. Robert wanted to admit Mrs. Marla for evaluation of abdominal distention. She was coming from one of the nursing homes in an ambulance. When she arrived, I promptly went to her room and started to get her history. She was eighty-nine years old and a sweet old lady. She was uncomfortable and did not want to talk much, so I tried to be as brief as I could. I examined her and found the reason for her problem! She had not gone to the bathroom in six days, and every time she tried it hurt!

I called Dr. Robert and told him I was sure her problem could be solved easily with an enema. He asked me how many elderly patients with this problem I had seen. I said none. "Well, young man, have you heard of fecal impaction?" he asked. I said no. Then he told me that I would have to remove the impaction manually and then use my enema followed by a stool softener. This was certainly not what I was expecting, but I complied, took care of the problem, and transformed the sweet lady into a swearing monster, but accomplished the mission. After all was done, Chris just looked at me and laughed.

I went back to the room, and Enrique asked me how my day was. I said just fine. He, on the other hand, was thrilled. He had just been first assistant in a hysterectomy, and he could not help but tell me all about it. I just sat down at the desk, listened, and decided to write Tere a letter and bring her up to date on our adventure. Obviously, I did not write about my first case.

The next morning, after breakfast, I met with Chris, and we made rounds on our patients. Each belonged to a different attending physician, so we waited for each one to show up to discuss their patients. It was interesting to see how each attending physician had different ideas. I enjoyed being exposed to such a variety of styles and personalities. All of them had their own practices, and they knew their patients well; medicine seemed very personal to them. Interacting with them was an invaluable experience.

The week went fast; I admitted a few patients and followed them closely, and I even got to do a couple of discharges. Every day I would see

Dr. Cesare looking through my charts; he never said a word, but I knew he was watching my work. I even tried to write very clearly, which was not one of my best traits, so that he would be impressed.

We were now in our third week, and we were paged to Dr. Cesare's office. Enrique and I got there, and his secretary told us to go right in. As we entered his office, he was sitting in his chair, grinning and holding two brand-new name tags in his hands. One for me and one for Enrique, both with the word *intern* behind our names! He told us that we would be added to the call roster, and he was sure we would do fine. We were also sure our fellow interns would be happy to take fewer calls once we were on the schedule.

Being a total of seven interns, we would be on call every sixth night since one of us would be in the ER at night were we took a week at a time. This was not bad at all. Dr. Cesare also told us that we would rotate four months in internal medicine, four months in surgery, and two months in each obstetrics and pediatrics. Throughout the year we would also take night call in the ER, one week every seven weeks.

Chris was excited to hear the news about fewer calls and immediately started to divide the patients in the service between the two of us. In the future I would have my own patients, and she would have hers. From here on it all went well; every day we would do the rounds on our patients, discuss them with the attending, and do all the procedures that needed to be done. Most of the time we would be done by noon, and we alternated any new admissions between the two of us. In the afternoons, we would recheck on our patients, and most of the time we would be done by 3:00 p.m. Then we would all meet in the ER, help to clear the waiting room, and then check out to the one on call. Most days we were ready to leave by 5:00 p.m.

During my rotation in internal medicine, I also learned about the teaching service. When an admission was needed for a patient with no insurance, the patient would be admitted to the teaching service, which meant we were totally in charge without an attending physician, but always supervised and advised by Dr. Frank. It was a good feeling to realize that these patients were our responsibility and that the hospital would consider them charity care, and they would not be charged or be given a discount. It was a way for the hospital to give back to the community.

This was a type of medical care I had never been exposed to before. With the hospital being in a mostly middle-class community, most of the patients had insurance. The majority did not have to pay anything, and others had a fixed percent of their bill that they were responsible for. Patients who would need hospitalization or came through the ER and who were uninsured would be considered charity cases and would be admitted to the teaching service. The business office would determine how much they could afford and set up a payment plan, or if they had no resources they would get free care.

I was very curious about how this worked for the hospital. It was explained to me that the hospital received funds for construction or maintenance through the Hill-Burton Act, and in return they agreed to provide free care or reduced charges to a certain number of patients every year. This seemed like a win-win situation for both the patients and the hospitals.

The Hill-Burton Act was passed by Congress in 1946; the law gave hospitals, nursing homes, and other health facilities grants and loans for construction and modernization. In return, they agreed to provide a reasonable volume of services to persons unable to pay and to make their services available to all persons residing in the facility's area. Participation in Medicare and Medicaid was also on the list of requirements for access to Hill-Burton funding. In the early 1970s, lawyers representing poor people began suing hospitals for not abiding by the law; the law was amended in 1973. The most significant changes at this point were the addition of more regulations; unfortunately, the program was allowed to expire and stopped providing funds in 1997.

My next three months in internal medicine went uneventfully; I learned something every day. My only regret was that anytime we had a patient who needed to be in intensive care, we would transfer their care to the residents from Boston, even though we were allowed to follow these patients, we were rarely involved in their care. Some residents would spend time teaching us; others dismissed us as the foreign guys.

My next rotation was obstetrics. Framingham had a relatively relaxed service; there were four to five babies born daily. It was definitely very different from my clinical obstetric rotation in Mexico. Our job was to admit the patient, decide whether she was in labor, and then call the obstetrician at his or her office. Then the obstetrician would decide whether to come in or let us do a vaginal exam and check for dilatation. The majority of obstetricians told us to go ahead, and depending on dilatation and whether this was the patient's first baby, they would decide when they would come in.

The nursing staff was wonderful; they were unceasingly kind and competent. They never appeared rushed; it was a well-run service. Ms. Claire, the charge nurse, ran a tight ship; things got done or else! I never saw a patient leave without praising the nurses and being happy with the experience in the labor ward.

Things were very different from what I had been exposed to in Mexico. Here once the patients were admitted in labor, they would be started on what was called a "labor cocktail." This was a combination of a narcotic, and antiemetic, and scopolamine. The mixture of the three drugs created a state in which the woman, while responding somewhat to pain, did not remember it after delivering her baby. It was called "twilight sleep" and was in vogue in obstetrics in the 1970s.

Labors were long, and we would check the cervix every couple of hours. After it had become completely dilated, the patient was taken to the delivery room. A spinal anesthesia was given by the anesthesiologist, and the baby was delivered, most of the time by an easy forceps pull. The mothers were usually too drugged to push their babies out. Once the baby was delivered, the obstetrician would check him or her out and would go out to the waiting room. He would then announce to the husband and the family that the baby was a healthy boy or girl, and everybody would celebrate.

The father was not allowed to see the mother for a couple of hours till she was awake and then they were sent to a postpartum room. The baby in the meantime was transferred to the nursery, given a bath, and placed at the window for the family to view. It was not unusual to see babies that were very sleepy for hours after delivery.

The babies would come back to the rooms at four-hour intervals to be fed by bottle or to nurse, which was not very frequent. No visitors were allowed during feeding time, except for the fathers. If all went well, on the fifth day the mother and baby would be discharged to go home.

It was a little bit of a shock to me. I had seen women laboring awake and many times even walking. I was used to shorter labors and babies being pushed out by their mothers, and frequently these babies would be nursing immediately after delivery. But I was told this was progress; labor was painless, and women did not remember the experience and went home happy.

During my obstetrical rotation, I met some wonderful obstetricians. The two I recall the most were Dr. Paul, who patiently taught me how to apply forceps and the safe way to use them. He was a patient man; he did not mind me fumbling trying to figure out the right branch from the left or whether they were upside down. He would just correct me and let me try again. I was glad the patients never remembered anything!

Dr. Paul also became a very good friend; he taught Enrique, who by that time had become "Henry," and me how to cross-country ski and took us downhill skiing once. Unfortunately, I made a fool of myself trying to get up the hill on the ski tow. Somehow, I could not keep my skis straight for very long and would get off it where I was not supposed to, making a real mess. Finally, when I got to the top of the beginner's hill, I aimed straight down just to pick up too much speed and then tumbled down the rest of the hill. It took several tries for me to learn how to control my speed and come down safely. I think by that time everybody else had left the hill for fear of being run into by me.

Dr. Paul also invited us to his home for dinner on several occasions; it was nice to have food other than the cafeteria food. After eating there every day for months, we knew exactly what was on the menu each day. We also got to meet Dr. Paul's family and made good friends. I played the guitar and sang for them after dinner; they really liked my Mexican songs.

In return, he taught us how to chop wood, and we would make sure they always had plenty of wood for the fireplace.

The other obstetrician I remember well was Dr. Orville; he was an interesting man. Besides being an obstetrician, he owned a funeral home and did some of the mortician work himself. But he was one of the best clinicians I ever met. He would spend a lot of time with me teaching me how to determine the baby's position in the uterus, just by careful exam. He also worked with me on my vaginal exams. For him, feeling the cervix, its character, and position was the clue to telling how long a labor was going to last. He had an unusual practice that I did not share; he did all his exams without gloves. He always argued that with his bare hand he could feel things better. I will have to say he was always right!

The obstetrics department also ran a free prenatal clinic. It was for people who could not afford care, and the population was mostly young women, many of them students with unplanned pregnancies. The clinic ran every Wednesday. It was run by the interns supervised by a volunteer obstetrician. There was a different supervisor every month. We would take the role of the primary doctor, and the obstetrician would work with us. It was a great experience. One of my patients was a thirteen-year-old who was in her last month of pregnancy. I got to follow her in clinic, which she attended alone since her parents did not want to be involved. Eventually, I got to be there for the delivery of her baby, which she had agreed to give up for adoption.

It was very hard to see this thirteen-year-old girl go through a very difficult time all alone. So against my better judgment, I got emotionally involved and tried to help her through her hospital stay. I even talked to her parents and met with her after her discharge several times until her family decided to move away with the hope of giving her a fresh start. This seemed to be a good decision for all. I have always wondered what happened to her after that.

Obstetrics turned out to be a fun rotation. I absolutely loved being in the delivery room, with the anticipation, the adrenaline pumping, and then seeing a brand new human being come into this world screaming.

That was fun! I also think that the nursing staff and the obstetricians made it an enjoyable time. The two months I spent in obstetrics did not seem long enough. But it was time to move on again.

It was now the end of April, and finally the weather was warming up. We had experienced plenty of the New England winter. We had snow from Thanksgiving to the middle of March; we skied, skated, and even fished through a hole in the ice of Learned Pond next to the hospital. It was definitely time for some warmer weather, and things were turning beautiful!

This kind of spring was something we had never seen before. In Mexico City the weather does not change much all year; here spring made everything bloom! We learned about crocuses and daffodils, lilacs, yellow forsythias, and flowering trees. Up to this time we had never left Framingham, but now were ready to explore the New England sights we had been hearing about from the nurses.

Unfortunately, there was also sadness in my heart. I had written many letters to Tere, but I had not gotten any back; it was like she had disappeared. I even tried a couple of phone calls to no avail. I could not do anything about it, so I decided I would not let it bother me and enjoy the people around me. Framingham Union Hospital had a School of Nursing, and we had made many friends among the students. There was actually a cute physical therapist that I was particularly fond of.

Giovanna was the therapist's name; she was cute and seemed to always be happy and smiling. We spent some good times together. Many months later, when I was back home, she came to Mexico City and stayed at my parents' house. We showed her around the city, and I took her out many times. We had a good time, and I really enjoyed her company. I think she liked me more than I liked her. We never crossed paths again.

I started my surgical rotation, and I was looking forward to being involved in some major surgeries. I had already met some of the surgeons during my ER calls. I especially liked two of them, Dr. Jeremiah and Dr. Maurice. Both were great teachers, and I had learned how to suture and do "invisible" stitches that hopefully left no scars. I got to repair plenty of lacerations; the nurses knew I was good with children, so I got called many times to come down to the ER to suture a child. When I was off, since most of the time we did not go out, I used to hang around the ER and help out.

Surgery was busy! Surgeons like to start their days early. Most days we would start in the operating room at 7:00 a.m. We were assigned to several cases through the day. First we worked as second assistants, but as time went on some surgeons would let us first assist and even do some minor procedures. We would then follow our patients to the recovery room and then in the surgical ward till they went home. In the evenings we would meet the patients who would be having surgery the next morning, and we would do a thorough history and physical exam and document it in the record. We were also in charge of checking all the preoperative blood work and make sure everything was in order.

I became good friends with Dr. Murray; he was a neurosurgeon with the most optimistic personality I have ever encountered. He was determined to convince me to go into neurosurgery. I helped him in many of his cases and was fascinated by many of the surgeries done under the microscope. His dexterity was amazing; he also used to joke all the time. As he looked through the microscope, he would say things like "Oops! I can see the patient is having some bad thoughts; I better hurry up." Unfortunately, many of his patients had brain tumors or severe head injuries and did not always do well. I guess his sense of humor was some sort of defense.

The other surgeon whom I got to know well was Dr. Julius; he was a pediatric surgeon. He was not only a very capable surgeon, but he was also great dealing with children. He was also very good with the parents; it was not unusual for him to sit with the parents after surgery and reassure them that everything was going to be OK. He was also a hugger; he would hug everybody, patients, parents, nurses, and even we interns got a hug once in a while! He coined the name *Jorge, El Magnífico*, which he said was my Mexican bullfighter's name. Unfortunately, this name stuck with the pediatric staff, and I became El Magnífico throughout my stay.

What impressed me more than anything about these surgeons was the "culture," as we call it nowadays. They were very involved with their patients. They were not what I always thought surgeons were: glorified technicians with large egos. They knew their patients well, came to their bedsides every day, and spent time with them. When the referring physicians would stop by to visit their patients, which they did often, they would give them progress reports. There was a very personal relationship between the doctors and the patients.

By now it was the middle of the summer; we had been to Boston and visited the USS *Constitution*, Bunker Hill, and the Boston Tea Party ship. We drove to Plymouth and visited Plymouth Rock and the *Mayflower II*, and we also drove along the coast to Gloucester, where we had lobster for the first time in our lives. I was fascinated by the historic richness of the area. It seemed like everywhere we went there was something interesting to learn.

Unfortunately, there were two things that drove me absolutely crazy about the New England summer. First the humidity: I had never been in eighty-five degrees Fahrenheit with 90 percent humidity; it was suffocating. Second, the daylight: There were days that it was eight o'clock at night, and the sun was still out. It was a good season though; we made many friends, among the physician staff and the nursing students. We partied almost every weekend during the summer!

My surgical rotation came to an end, and it was time for my last rotation in the pediatric ward. Somehow pediatrics always seemed to come last. This was a very different service; the pediatric ward was a happy place, painted in bright colors and with many cartoon characters on the walls. The nursing staff was a pleasure to work with; they always seemed to be upbeat. Carol, the head nurse, was a very experienced nurse, but the rest of the staff was young. Paula, Mary, and Helen were my favorites. Every night when I was off, I would bring my dinner and sit with the nurses and chat. They also had a refrigerator with free cokes for the patients; somehow, I always seemed to get one, too. Carol told me on my last week that I would have to come back and work for free for a year to pay for the more than two thousand cokes I drank. Of course she was kidding!

Pediatricians were a unique breed of doctor; they always seemed to be upbeat. They would come and see their patients and then go back to their office, sometimes several times a day. Never seemed to get involved in hospital stuff. As long as their patients were taken care off they were fine. I got to meet many of them. Most of the children they would admit to the hospital were easy to take care of. Diarrhea and dehydration were common during my first month, but in October, as soon as the weather started cooling off, we saw many children with breathing problems. I have always been good at starting IVs, so the nurses would always call me when a young child was admitted even if I was off.

That was the advantage of living right next to the hospital and not going out much at night. Any time the nurses needed an extra hand either in the ER or in pediatrics, the phone would ring and somebody would say, "Are you doing anything important?" I actually loved these phone calls; it gave me the opportunity to do more and learn more.

One night it was late, and I had just gotten to bed when Dr. Gilbert, a pediatrician, called me on the phone and said, "I know you are off, but would you like to learn how to do an exchange transfusion?" I jumped out of bed and was at the pediatric ward in less than a minute! This was exciting, an exchange transfusion! Wow! This was a newborn with Rh isoimmunization and rising bilirubin; the procedure needed to be done immediately. We discussed the amount and type of blood needed and had the blood bank have it ready.

Then he showed me how to put an umbilical venous line and how to set up the system. Then he told me we would exchange 10 ml at the time, and the nurse would keep track until we got to the prescribed amount of 630 ml. It needed to be done slowly to allow time for mixing. Then he handed me the system and told me, "Pull the line out when you are done" and went to sleep in the call room. At 10 ml each pass and 630 ml that was sixty-three passes, which took about three minutes each; over three hours all together! I knew right away that I had been suckered in! It was a good learning experience anyway.

Again, I found out that I really liked pediatrics; I seemed to relate well to children and had no problem talking to parents. The Framingham pediatricians taught me that just being there meant a lot to the parents. Even though we would do all the admission paperwork and exams and orders, they would invariably come in and reassure the parents, look over our notes, and sign them.

Medicine was a very personal thing for all the doctors in Framingham; if I learned something from my internship this was probably the one thing that I would always remember. Somehow, the tiny town outside Mexico City and the middle-class small town in the United States were not very different. The center of the medical community was the patient; for doctors, nurses, and administrators making sure that the patient was taken care of was the goal. The rest just seemed to fall in place.

But all good things come to an end. It was the end of October, and even though the colors were beautiful outside and the air was crisp and fall had just begun, our time in Framingham was coming to an end. We had made some good friends and learned a lot, but we still had a year to pay back to Mexico before we were free to decide where our future would take us.

My last two weeks in pediatrics I spent orienting a new intern. His name was Dr. Emilio, and he was from Italy. I remembered how Dr. Chris had helped me at the beginning, so it was my turn to return the favor. He had the same trouble I had reading charts, so I passed on to him the code sheet that I had made a year before. It was time for us to pass on the responsibilities to the new interns and say good-bye.

The nurses and student nurses seemed particularly friendly toward me those last two weeks. I got a lot of invitations to go out. I ended up spending a lot of time with one in particular. Her name was Susan, a cute, short, blond ICU nurse. One night she suggested that we go up to my room. I was afraid that Henry would show up any minute, so we went to Shigeru's room, as I knew he would not be there that night. We spent the night together, and early in the morning she slipped out. The next morning as I walked through the hospital, I saw many sly smiles everywhere; I found out later that word had gotten out that I was a virgin, and I had been the subject of a bet. It was rather embarrassing!

On our last weekend, I went around the hospital with my tape recorder and recorded the nurses' and doctors' voices and their names. I had some very nice farewell messages. I still listen to them once in a while; it is nice to remember all these wonderful people.

We met with Dr. Cesare, and he gave us our letters of completion and told us, "Jorge and Henry, you have a good heart, a good mind, and are accumulating knowledge; there is nothing you cannot do in your medical careers." I will forever remember his words. He rated us as "excellent," which would translate into another 100 for our university score.

So on October 31, we walked out of Framingham Union Hospital not to ever go back again.

Chapter 5
SOCIAL SERVICE YEAR

We arrived back in Mexico City in the evening, and at the airport Enrique and I went our separate ways for the first time in a year. Our families were waiting for us, and they each had plans for welcome parties for us. We hugged and said our goodbyes and went on to celebrate our triumphant returns. Enrique's girlfriend Blanca was there; Tere was nowhere to be found. It is sad to think that I would not see Enrique again but for a few more times in Mexico. We did our social service year with the same company but in different places; he eventually went into obstetrics, married Blanca, and became a renowned obstetrician in Mexico City.

I had a wonderful welcome party just like anything my mother ever organized. There was a table full of Mexican food; I had not had anything like that in a whole year. It was so nice to be home again. It was so good to see my parents and both my brothers with their spouses and my sister. Tere eventually showed up, but I did not have much desire to talk to her; we exchanged a few words, but no more than that. I had a lot to be happy for and was not going to let her spoil it.

Now it was time to think of where I was going to do my social service year. This year of service is a requirement of the Mexican Government. Mexico is one of the few countries that have a mandatory service component for students enrolled in higher education. This requirement benefits marginalized sectors of society while raising students' awareness and deepening their sense of social responsibility. This mandatory service requirement was established in the national constitution in 1910.

Most graduate medical students go to small towns where they provide medical care for a year. This is usually done through an institution like the IMSS, the Health Department, or other government agencies. Petróleos Mexicanos (trademarked and better known as PEMEX), the Mexican state-owned petroleum company, also offers social service opportunities. These positions are to provide medical care to its employees, usually in remote work locations and offshore platforms. Most of them start January 1, so I had a couple of months to apply. PEMEX was where I wanted to work.

I submitted my application and then gathered recommendation letters from several people. One in particular was from my uncle who worked at a government agency and was very well connected. He promised to make a few calls on my behalf, and I also got a nice letter from him. In Mexico sometimes what is important is not what you know but who you know. I had good grades, and a good rating for my internship, but I needed a little extra help to get the position I wanted.

Needless to say I got it! And Enrique did too; we were going to work at PEMEX.

We were assigned to the district of Poza Rica in the northern part of the state of Veracruz. This district includes the offshore drilling plat-forms, also known as oil rigs, in the Gulf of Mexico, and the exploration camps spread out throughout the state. We were to meet at the zone hospital in Poza Rica, where we would learn about our assignments. Both Enrique and I were assigned to exploration camps in different locations. I was assigned to the one located in Tierra Blanca, which is about sixty miles south of city of Veracruz and about forty miles inland from the Gulf of Mexico.

Exploration camps are semipermanent camps. Housing is somewhat like mobile homes; each unit was about fifteen by fifteen feet, made out of wood, usually with a door and four windows. They were set up over one-foot concrete pylons, and they were otherwise empty. Each usually accommodated four to six workers except for the one assigned to the doc-tor, which also served as an office. Bathrooms were in separate units, as well as the mess hall, which was three units together, with one serving as the kitchen.

These camps are the operation center of seismic surveying crews. These crews are usually hundreds of people, deployed over vast areas for many months. They take an area of land where oil is likely to be found and divided into grids. A clearing crew goes first and clears this grid from trees and then the perforation crew follows, drilling a test well and placing dynamite in it. The geology crew then places sensors and detonates the dynamite while detecting and recording the seismic activity produced by the explosions. Dynamite is regarded as the ideal geophysical source due to it producing almost perfect impulses, allowing geologists to map and interpret potential petroleum reservoirs.

These survey operations require substantial logistical support. In addition to the day-to-day seismic operation itself, there must also be support for the main camp (for catering, waste management, laundry, etc.), and smaller temporary camps (e.g., where the distance is too far to drive back to the main camp with all the equipment), as well as vehicle and equipment maintenance, medical personnel, and security. I was the "medical support" for the entire operation.

We, meaning the entire camp personnel, worked three weeks on and one week off; after three weeks of work the camp closed, and everybody went home for a week. That seemed to be a very acceptable deal for the workers, and they made good money. Unfortunately, many of them spent it all during their week off.

My first three weeks were spent at the main camp; I would just go around meeting people and figuring out what I could do. I did not get much activity in my office; an occasional worker would come looking for cold medicine or an aspirin for a headache, but nothing major. We were also under the obligation of being available to the people in the surrounding community although they did not belong to PEMEX. We were even encouraged to charge for these visits. The camp was so close to a small town that already had a doctor, that I never had any patients from outside the camp.

Then things started to change. When I came back for my second tour, the next area to be mapped was El Moral, and it was far from the camp.

So I was told we would go to a temporary advanced camp to be close to the work site. We packed our bags and my medical supplies and there we went. When we arrived in El Moral there was nothing there but an old palm-roofed house. Within two hours the support personnel erected several tents and built a temporary mess hall, basically a roof over a few tables, a kitchen, and when I asked where should I put my stuff they told me my accommodation was going to be the old house where I could have my office.

Everybody laughed at my expression but told me that it was the best they could give me, so I moved in. The house had a partition, so I asked them to set up my bed on one side and my desk and supplies on the other side. The supplies were on three wooden boxes that also served as shelves. The floor was dirt and the walls made out of wood slats tied together. There were two window-like openings and an entrance without a door. This would be home for the next three weeks. Oh my!

It turned not to be not as bad as I feared; my house was actually much cooler than the workers' tents, and since they had sprayed repellant around it, I did not have to worry about critters visiting me. Snakes are particularly plentiful in that area, so the entire camp perimeter was sprayed. The first few nights, I did not sleep much and heard every noise around, but I got used to it quickly.

As soon as the locals found out that there was a doctor at the camp I started getting visits, most of them easy gastrointestinal problems related to parasites. Many would actually bring me what they had passed. Not a pretty site but it was helpful to diagnose them and prescribe a treatment. I got an occasional cut that I had to suture or a girl wondering if she was pregnant. Since I had no lab and pregnancy tests sticks did not exist then, all my diagnosis had to be made clinically. They put my skills to the test.

I charged five pesos a visit, which many could not pay, so many times I took less or nothing for my services. Many times they would bring me things like eggs, chickens, plantains, or even homemade tamales. I always had to take these presents since they would be offended otherwise. I took home most of my gifts, but I drew the line when I was given a goat. The cook took it, and we had *cabrito asado* (roasted goat) that night. These people always seemed so thankful that I would see them that I was humbled.

About the second week, one night about midnight, one of the workers came to wake me up and told me that there was an emergency at one of the ranches close by. A woman had been in labor for two days, and the baby was not coming. They had brought two horses for me to ride back. I had become a good friend with this particular worker. His name was Tomás. He told me he was not allowed to let me go alone, so he would go with me. I packed everything I thought I might need and climbed on a horse along with Tomás; the rancher walked all the way back.

When I arrived, this young girl, probably in her twenties, was lying on a *petate* (a mat made of woven palm leaves), and there was no light in the room, only candles. There were about six women in the house, so I asked all of them to leave except the mother, and I proceeded to examine my patient. She was in obvious labor and having frequent contractions. Unfortunately, it was what I suspected; it was a breech birth. I could palpate the head in the upper part of the uterus. The good thing was that the baby had a strong heartbeat. I explained to the girl and the mother that I was going to have to do a vaginal exam to try to help the baby come out. It took a bit of convincing, but I did and confirmed my diagnosis.

I did not have the means to do a C-section, so my only choice was to get her to relax and help her push the baby out. I knew how important it was to not rush a breech delivery so that the head would not get trapped afterward. I gave her a small dose of Demerol, just to relax her, and I put a few drops of oxytocin on a cotton ball and put it in her nose. I had to be careful not to give her too much, so I put my hand on her abdomen and monitored the contractions and listened to the baby every so often. When the contractions improved, we helped her into the squatting position and encouraged her to push with the contractions. Two of the women, one of them being the partera (midwife), came in to help her hold on. I was sweating!

About an hour later, I could see the breech protruding; I refrained from doing anything but continued to reassure everybody. As the breech came out, I asked her to lie down and then I freed the legs one by one while rotating the body, and as the chest came out I reached for the arms one at a time and freed both of them. It was thanks to Dr. Paul at Framingham, who had showed me how to deliver a breech. Then it was the head, probably the most difficult part; I allowed time for it to come, but it did not seem to move. I asked the midwife to hold the body up while I applied a set of forceps to the head. They were not the correct kind, but they did the job and the head came out! I cut the cord and he cried!

I was so thankful and relieved. I don't think I had been that scared in my life before. The rest went smoothly; the placenta came out, and I gave her a dose of methergin to contract the uterus, and she did well. The mother promised me that they would name the baby after me; a week later I was invited to the baptism of Jorge Augusto. It was scary, but one of the best experiences of my life.

As we returned to camp, everybody had heard the story, so that evening after work we all celebrated with beer, mescal, and *botanas*. I, unfortunately, drank more than I should have and paid dearly for it the next morning. It probably cured me from ever drinking too much again.

During my stay in the Tierra Blanca area, I delivered five more babies, all of them healthy. I should actually say I watched over their deliveries, as my father used to say, "When all goes well, watching a woman deliver is a beautiful thing to do." Anyway, I was very proud of my obstetrical skills.

When I went home this time, I had saved most of the money from my paycheck, so I bought myself a used Jeep. I figured it would give me more mobility than riding a horse! When I returned to Tierra Blanca, I was proud to show off my beautiful vehicle. Full metal cab, metal doors, four-wheel drive, and a rack; it became very handy because I could pack all my supplies and take them anywhere I needed to go.

In the next three weeks, we moved to a new advance camp, this time in a place called Las Charcas, about forty miles further south. By the time I drove there, the camp was already set up; again I got a palm shack. Even though it was smaller than the previous one, it was still better than the tents the workers were in.

This time we were close to a fairly large creek with relatively clear water, so I would drive my jeep to it and bathe there. At the camp there was only a makeshift shower, which was an elevated tank with an opening that was attached to a string, so it was not the best. On my way I had to drive by the home of the family who actually owned the land; they did not mind at all. They were ecstatic to have the doctor come to bathe in their creek. The owner Don Antonio was about sixty years old and had one daughter and eight sons. The daughter was fifteen, and the youngest boy was just seven months.

I went there almost every morning, and sometimes the three younger boys, Victoriano, Lucio, and Fidel, would jump in the Jeep and accompany me. The oldest of them, Victoriano, who was about eleven years old, was quite inquisitive. He always had a million questions for me about where I came from. He had never been away from home, and he was very curious. One day, on my way back, Antonio insisted that I stay for lunch. They had prepared what I thought was chicken in mole sauce and even bought me a couple of beers. Eventually, I found out that the meat was actually snapping turtle; I was pleasantly surprised. I had a really good time with them.

Back at the camp things were quiet; the doctor was rarely needed. I spent a lot of time with the supply guy and the kitchen workers. I had a couple of deliveries to attend to and an occasional walk-in from nearby ranches, but never a real emergency or a difficult case.

Almost at the end of my tour, while at Antonio's house, Teresa, the fifteen-year-old daughter, told me she had a present for me. It was a baby parrot they had been raising by hand when she fell off the nest, and she wanted me to take it home. I was surprised that she would give it to me, so I made them a deal; I invited one of the boys to my house in Mexico City for a week. That way he would help me bring the parrot home. Victoriano immediately asked if he could go. Taking him home turned out to be one of the best experiences of my life.

As I headed home, I stopped to pick up Victoriano, and the whole family was waiting for me. Mother gave him lots of advice, and Antonio gave me permission to beat him up if he misbehaved. I told him I would bring him back safe, not to worry. We got in the Jeep, and I decided to just drive to Tierra Blanca, spend the night in a hotel, and drive to Mexico City the next morning. As he got in the Jeep I noticed he had only a small bag with some underwear. I asked him if that was all he was bringing, and he told me that was all he had! He was wearing some old tennis shoes, no socks, and a shirt and pants.

Our first stop was at a department store; I bought him new shoes, a couple of new shirts, and pants, pajamas, underwear, and something he had never had: several pairs of socks. We also bought a small suitcase, a comb, toothbrush, and a cage for the parrot, which we named Teresa. He was glowing when we left the store, and when we got to the hotel he wanted to try them all. It was fun watching him. But that was just the beginning of the surprises we were going to have together.

The first thing he noticed at the hotel was the bed; he had never slept on a bed in his life. At home everybody slept on petates on the floor. He was amazed; he would roll back and forth and could not get over how soft it was. Then we went to get some dinner at a local restaurant. I quickly realized that he could not read when I handed him the menu, and he looked at it not knowing what he was supposed to do. I asked him what he liked, and we settled on chicken enchiladas, which he devoured in a few minutes. He also enjoyed a coke and ice cream for dessert.

As we returned to the hotel, I asked him if he wanted to take a shower. I felt he needed it! He went into the bathroom and came out after a minute and told me he could not find the water. So I went in and showed him how to turn the water on and how to adjust the temperature of the water. Watching his face was priceless; he had never seen a shower, and hot water coming out of the wall was a miracle to him. I gave him soap and showed him the towels and went back to the room. Thirty minutes later, I could still hear the water, so I went in again and he was just enjoying himself. I told him to get out and dry himself, put on his pajamas, and go to bed. He finally turned the water off!

The next morning at around 5:00 a.m., just as the sun was peeking out, I heard the water running in the bathroom. Victoriano was in the shower again! He was absolutely fascinated with it; I had to almost bribe him to get him to come out and get dressed. We went for breakfast and got on the road to Mexico City.

It was about a four-and-a half-hour drive. He did not know where to look; everything was new to him, and he asked questions about everything he saw. You could feel the excitement in his voice; this was a completely new world to him. But nothing was more astounding than getting into Mexico City. He had never seen more than three cars in one place; there were thousands of them all around him. He was standing up in the jeep and just could not believe what he was looking at. It took some time for him to settle down; by the time we arrived at my parents' house he was exhausted.

The week was one exciting adventure after another for Victoriano; he saw magic in everything we take for granted. From movies to pizza everything was new to him. Taking Victoriano home was one of the best experiences of my life; I will never forget it.

My mother decided she could not let him go back without learning to read, so she spent a couple of hours with him every day. He knew his letters and he learned quickly, so by the end of the week he could read simple words and sound out more difficult ones. My mother was really proud of his progress. She never said anything, but I could see it in her eyes that she would have loved to keep him forever if she could. The day we went back her eyes were teary as she hugged him tight. Teresa the parrot stayed home, and my mother loved her and spoiled her until she died at the age of thirty-two.

When we went back to Tierra Blanca, I took Victoriano home before going to the PEMEX camp. Everybody in his family was happy to see him; there were lots of hugs and kisses, and they could not wait to hear all about his trip. As I was getting ready to leave, I started to wonder if I had done the right thing by taking him home. I was not quite sure, at that time, what effect the trip would have on him. I did get a letter from him a year later. He was going to school regularly and was reading and writing well. He told me when he grew up he wanted to go to medical school like me.

When I arrived at the Tierra Blanca Camp, I was told that we would be going to a new advanced camp at a location known as La Piedra Lagoon. It was further south to our previous camp and fairly isolated. The area was mostly marshes and shallow lagoons. There were not many people living in the area, but they still managed to come to the camp to find the doctor. Unfortunately, this time I had to share my shack with two of the engineers, so I did not have an office to see the patients. So many times I did my consultations out in the open under a tree.

The area was composed of wetlands that were continually inundated with fresh water; green areas with vegetation would alternate with clear-water lagoons. Water levels varied from a few inches to two or three feet, except in the middle of the lagoons where it could be as much as six to eight feet deep. The usual drilling equipment could not be used; so they would use these vehicles with huge tires that could move easily in mud and float in water. I joined the work crews a couple of times; it was very interesting to watch.

Unfortunately, there were more mosquitos and biting flies there than I had ever experienced. My only trip to the nearest town was to buy a mosquito tent to put over my bed. Sometimes, I would hide in it even during the day. I was the envy of the two engineers who shared my shack. There was no such thing as repellant, but the workers taught me how to use mud on one's exposed areas to keep from being bitten. Not a very pretty method but definitely efficient.

As we approached the end of the three-week tour, I was told that they had gotten to the end of the mapping of that area, and the camp was going to be closed and dismantled. I would be reassigned to either another camp or to the offshore platforms. Part of me was sad because I had enjoyed working in the camps. I had not only been able to be responsible for my crew, but I had also been allowed to practice medicine, which I had enjoyed immensely. As rudimentary as it was it was very personal and a lot of fun. On the other hand, my professional exam was approaching, and I needed time to study; I had heard that free time was plentiful in the offshore rigs.

One afternoon, I drove back to Las Charcas to see Antonio and his family. They were all happy to see me and invited me to stay for dinner.

This time I was treated to a new dish: Iguana! These lizards grow to be five to six feet in Veracruz, and their tails are very meaty. I was able to watch as they prepared it. I learned that for Iguana meat to taste good it has to be boiled in saltwater for twenty minutes before stewing it. They cooked this one in a pozole stew; it was delicious! I never had it again in my lifetime; Iguana meat is illegal in the United States.

Antonio was very friendly this time; after a few beers he told me he wanted me to take his fifteen-year-old daughter with me this time. He explained to me that I did not have to bring her back and that she would make me a good wife and give me many children. I politely declined his offer and hurried back to my camp. I knew his intentions were sincere, but I was not ready for that.

On the last day of our tour, I drove back to the Tierra Blanca camp and talked to the administrator. I had been reassigned to the Atun block of offshore oilrigs. I was to report in one week to the Poza Rica office from where I would be flown by helicopter to my new post in the Atun B platform. My schedule this time would be fifteen days on and fifteen days off, and I would only be responsible for the health of the workers in the oilrig. It seemed that I would have plenty of time to study, but it was a little scary; I would be in an oilrig in the middle of the Gulf of Mexico. I would also be making more money because I would be getting a risk bonus added to my regular pay. It sounded good, but I had no idea of what I was getting into.

When I got home, my mother was not thrilled about the news, but there was nothing she could do. My father on the contrary was excited and wondered if there would be a chance for him to visit. I did not know if that was possible, but I promised I would ask.

A week later I was on my way in my Jeep to Poza Rica. This time I had to pack light, since I could only bring what I could carry. It was only a fifteen-day tour, so it was easy to pack everything in a small suitcase along with my notes and books to study and as always my trusty medical bag. On arrival, I was told where to park my Jeep, and immediately I was taken to the heliport and was on my way to Atun B. I did not have time to worry; we were on the move!

It took us about thirty minutes to reach Atun B; the platform was located on the continental shelf of the Gulf of Mexico, about twenty-five miles from the coast. The weather was beautiful, the sky was clear, and suddenly there it was; it looked like a cardboard box standing on six steel legs, with a tower on top. Not exactly what I wanted to call home for the next two weeks.

When we arrived, the helicopter just stopped long enough for me to get off carrying my suitcase in one hand and my medical bag in the other. The doctor I was replacing was waiting at the helipad; as I disembarked, he stopped by me for a second and said, "I left you a note!" and got into the helicopter. I felt a little bit lost as the helicopter took off again, but the oilrig administrator was there to welcome me.

Mr. Marcelo was the oilrig manager; he was a drilling engineer and the captain of the ship. He supervised all the staff on the oilrig as well as the drilling activities and equipment. He showed me to my room, which was located under the cardboard box separate from all the other living quarters, bathrooms, and the mess hall. The room was about twelve feet square, had a bed, a desk, two chairs, a couple of shelves with medications, an examining table, and a sink. A note on the desk read:

Welcome to Atun B, I will come back to replace you in fifteen days. This is the easiest job you have ever had; usually there is nothing to do, you will see a few colds, some VD (venereal disease), and occasionally an injury. The rule is that anything that looks contagious or serious needs to be evacuated. Otherwise, read, watch TV, and try to meet the staff. They are all nice people, and you will learn a lot from them. Good Luck.

David

Short and to the point!

I unpacked what I could and decided to go explore. The housing area had only one level. The engineer's quarters were two small rooms with two beds each. Then there was this large room that I was told was where the workers slept. It had twenty-four beds, and the night crew was sleeping at the moment. There were two more rooms for the cook and housekeeping crew. Then there was the bathroom, with six stalls, a common shower area, and twelve sinks with mirrors. The mess hall, the kitchen, and a small lounge with a TV were at the far end. There was a separate shed that housed the control room and the repair shop. The helipad was on top of the living quarters.

I learned that workers are on the job for twelve hours a day for seven straight days before they are given a weeklong break back on shore. There are two crews of twenty-four on the rig at all times: a night crew and a day crew. While one crew works the other one sleeps, and they share the same twenty-four beds. Each worker has a locker, where he keeps his bed sheets, which are washed once a week on crew change day. The routine works perfectly without a hitch. The kitchen crew prepares meals twenty-four hours a day, also in two shifts. There is breakfast, lunch, and dinner for both crews. Everybody seems to have a good attitude and get along.

The rigs operate day and night, seven days per week. Atun B was drilling twelve directional wells; they would drill for a while, then take core samples and adjust the direction. It was a fascinating process, and the engineers were always willing to teach and show me what was going on. I still own a piece of core obtained from a depth four thousand meters, which they gave me as a souvenir. I also spent time at the repair shop learning things like basic welding and engine repair. The most fun I spent was with the cooks; I knew nothing about cooking when I came on board, but by the end I had learned quite a bit.

My daily routine was very simple; I would get up and go upstairs to have breakfast with the day shift; then, after everybody showered and got in bed, I would take my shower. My strategy was to wait long enough so that I did not have to compete with a throng of naked bodies. After showering I would return to my room and study till lunchtime. In the afternoons and evenings I would visit with the crew, watch TV, or explore around my small world.

The only uncomfortable thing was that I did not have a bathroom, so for every necessity I had to walk up to the crew's living quarters. Well, not all the time; after a few days I learned that there were no women on the platform, so nobody cared if you elected to relieve yourself through the railing. The ocean was large, and there was no harm done. It was just important to check the direction of the wind beforehand.

One day, I was talked into going to the top of the tower. When they are either drilling or pulling the drill out there is always a worker on the top. He is called the *chango* (monkey), and he stands on the monkey board, which is a platform high up in the rig's tower. Alberto, one of the changos, guided me and helped me get there. It was a beautiful clear day, and I could see two other platforms and even a glimpse of land. It was scary but worth it; I wanted to stay for a long time, but when the wind started blowing, I changed my mind quickly.

My medical practice was very small, just like Dr. David had said in his note. A few colds, diarrhea, and, very frequently, when the workers came back from a week off I would treat some gonorrhea cases. It seemed that when the workers were on shore they spent their money on not-so-healthy activities. Only once was my expertise required. One of the drill pipes had gotten loose, and, as it bounced, it hit one of the workers on the head.

As I arrived at the scene of the accident, I knew he needed immediate evacuation. So I called for a helicopter. He had a depressed skull fracture, and there was fluid coming out of it. Not a good sign. I moved him to a stretcher and wrapped his head to protect the area, started an IV, and moved him to the helipad; he was unconscious. When the helicopter arrived we loaded him up, and I travelled with him. When we arrived at Poza Rica Hospital, I handed him over to the emergency crew and jumped back in the helicopter. Sadly, I heard a couple of days later that he had died. Mauricio was the first patient I ever lost; I could not sleep for days wondering if I could have done more.

On the fifteenth day, I was up early and packed my stuff. By ten in the morning, I was up on the helipad waiting. When the helicopter arrived, Dr. David got off, and I got on. This happened five more times until my year with PEMEX was over. It was a good experience, I had plenty of time to study, and I was ready to take my professional exam. My last day at Atun B was December 21, and my exam was scheduled for February 4.

My father and my eldest brother got to visit the platform. PEMEX had a program in which they were brought by the helicopter the day before I was to finish my tour; they spent the night with me on a not so comfortable cot and then we went back together the next day. Only male visitors were allowed; no woman was ever allowed on board. Actually, my brother got to go back on a boat rather than the helicopter because on that day bad weather was approaching, and the choppers were grounded. I think they both enjoyed their visits.

One never realizes what an impact one can have on other people's lives. Forty-three years later, through Facebook, Antonio's daughter Teresa found me, and we had an opportunity to talk about our lives since Las Charcas. She had married and had four children and now has grandchildren and even one great-grandchild. She had left home and lived in Mexico City for many years, where she had actually looked me up, but I had left for the United States. Then she moved to Cancun and eventually ended up in Delaware, where she currently lives. Victoriano never left Las Charcas and still lives there. He bought land and also has a large family and grandchildren. Forty-three years later, they both still remember the young doctor who somehow touched their lives.

Chapter 6

THE END OF MEDICAL SCHOOL AND THE SURPRISE OF A LIFETIME

I returned home and decided to take a week off from studying and tried to reconnect with my friends. I had dated several girls during my social service year, but none seemed special to me. My mother started calling me Don Juan, after the womanizing character in the Spanish play, because I seemed to date a different girl every time I came home. But I had many other things to think about, and I was not sure where medicine would take me next.

I had decided I wanted to do a pediatric residence, hopefully in the United States, so I sent all my papers to the National Resident Matching Program with the hope that I could get into a pediatric program. I had all the requirements needed; I had taken the exam of the Exchange Counsel for Foreign Medical Graduates (ECFMG) and obtained my certificate a year before. I had one year of experience at Framingham, and I was confident I would pass my professional exam. I was hoping to get a position in Texas so that I could take advantage of being bilingual. Unfortunately, residencies did not start till July, and the results of the matching program would not be available until April.

So I had to find something to do for six months. There were not very many options, but I managed to find a tiny little private hospital by the name of Sanatorio de Lourdes that was looking for an in-house physician to cover nights five days a week. The salary was reasonable, and I had to work only from Monday to Friday from seven in the evening to seven in the morning. My duty was to troubleshoot and take care of any problems or notify the attending physicians.

The job was easy; I got to sleep most nights, and the occasional problem was easy to solve, and I rarely bothered anybody. I went home in the mornings and had the rest of the day to study. As a bonus I had all weekends off. Little did I know that this job would change my life forever.

January went by quickly, and before I knew it, exam day was there!

Professional exams at that time in Mexico were very formal. You had a jury of five examiners, and each of them could ask you questions on a topic that you were assigned by lottery. The exam room was on the top floor of the Facultad de Medicina (Medical School) building. It was a kind of auditorium, and people could actually come and watch the exams from a distance. It all happens in one day; you are examined, and if you pass, you take the oath and then you are licensed to practice medicine on your own.

There were about twenty of us being examined that day; we were all formally dressed in suit and tie. One by one we approached the jury table and put our hands under what looks like a lottery ball machine and received a ball with a number, which translated into a topic. If you felt that it was not the best topic for you, you were allowed to draw again. I got number twenty–two, which was diseases of the liver; I felt I could handle it. I accepted it, and I was sent to the desk of my first examiner.

My first examiner happened to be Dr. Luis, my friend Georges's stepfather. He had a reputation of being tough. We shook hands, and he asked me to sit. I was sweating. Then he asked me to elaborate about liver disease. As I spoke, he interrupted me several times and would ask, "*Why?*" I would answer, and he would stop me again, "*Why?*," and this went on for about twenty minutes. Then he abruptly stopped me and said, "That is all I need. Thank you." He wrote on my evaluation card and handed it to the next examiner on his right and told me to go on. I sat with the second examiner; he looked at Dr. Luis's evaluation and said to me, "I am satisfied?" and sent me to the next examiner. The same thing happened with the next two examiners, and I was sent to the last one who was the chief examiner.

As I sat down he asked me, "If you had to pick one sign of liver disease, what would it be?" I said jaundice; he looked at me and smiled. Then he told me that in honor of my grandfather, who had been an examiner, and my father, a clinical professor, he wanted me to read the oath. I almost jumped out of my seat; I knew I had passed! So I told him I would be honored. We shook hands, and he sent me away. I could not help myself; I almost cried. My parents were in the audience, and I knew this would make them very proud.

When all the exams were finished, the chief examiner said a few words and called me to the front to read the oath. It was a moment that I would never forget; I still look at the picture and remember my parents standing up smiling. I was handed the oath by the chief examiner; I raised my right hand, and read:

Before the honorable jury that has examined me, and in the presence of this audience, I solemnly swear that I will contemplate human life as sacred, from conception to death and that I will make it the purpose of my life. I recognize the financial support provided by the community to this medical school, for my professional preparation. I will put all my effort and knowledge to achieve better health and hygiene in the places where I should dwell and in the exercise of my profession. I will always put the interests and the welfare of the patient before any personal egoism, comfort, or profit, and I will appreciate his life as my own or as more than, if necessary. I will keep silent about what could harm him and will consider inviolable his home and family.

In every doctor I will see a brother, and I will be a loyal colleague. I would always help him to treat sickness and in the vicissitudes of its existence, I will help him with brotherly concern and affection. I will respect his professional interests, and I will judge him with the indulgence required by our difficult healing art.

I am fortified by the principles of good conduct, self-denial, and avoidance of self-interest that my teachers taught me, and I will follow them all my life. If human weakness would make me hesitant, I will seek support in their venerable memories and in the tradition of nobility and such love that has been passed down for generations.

I solemnly swear to execute these vows for the honor of my homeland and school.

The same oath has been used for over sixty years. These were the same words my grandfather, my father, and my brother had recited. It was certainly an honor!

After the ceremony we were called one by one to sign the ledger and receive a temporary diploma. Our real diploma would not be ready for several weeks. Diplomas were hand written on real sheepskin with the university logo and the signatures of the secretary-general and the dean of the University. I got mine on April 15, 1974. It proudly hung in my office for over forty years, and now it hangs at home. I am still as proud of it now as I was then.

While waiting to hear from the matching program, I continued to work nights. Most nights were uneventful, and I never found any problem I could not resolve until the night of Tuesday, March 12.

It was the night that changed my life forever.

Around midnight, the nurse called me to see this patient who had rectal bleeding. She had had an appendectomy in the morning, and now she had a large amount of blood in her stools.

I walked into the room and saw this beautiful young woman with bright eyes, black hair, and a beautiful smile. She told me she felt fine; she had no pain at all. I examined her and apart the soreness in the abdomen from the surgery, everything seemed OK. There was definitely bright red blood in her stool, but she did not seem to be in any distress; so I decided to give her some time and just watch her.

I returned to her room about every two hours during the night, checked her blood pressure and pulse, and every time it all looked normal and she had not passed anymore more blood. I did my last check at seven in the morning; all seemed fine, so I finished my shift and went home.

But there was something about her that was different. Every time I would go in to check her, she would be smiling, and we would have a pleasant conversation, under the watchful eye of her mother, who was staying in a recliner in the room pretending to be asleep. I could not help but notice that she was very cute! I thought about her all day.

When I returned to work the next evening, I noticed her name was still on the list of patients; I looked through her record and noticed that she had been taken back to the operating room that morning for a revision of her appendectomy. The surgeon had resutured the stump, assuming that it was the origin of the blood and closed up uneventfully. I was looking for a good excuse to go see her when the nurse called me and said that she was having rectal bleeding again.

This time it was not just a little blood, but a considerable amount. I took her blood pressure and it was normal, but she looked a little pale and her pulse was also a little fast. I ordered a blood count and put a call out to her surgeon.

Her blood count results returned; her hematocrit was 22 percent, which is rather low, and she was still having large amounts of blood in her stool. The surgeon did not return my calls, and when I checked with the blood bank, they did not have any blood of her type available. I knew she was going to need it; I was starting to panic.

I talked to her family, which was rather large and justifiably angry. Her sister and brother asked me what I thought. I told them I could not do anything for her in that place, that she needed a facility with a better functioning blood bank and a surgeon to review her surgery. She needed to be transferred out!

Her sister was well connected to the IMSS, so they arranged for her to be transferred to the Centro Medico Nacional. An ambulance came, and I helped to expedite the discharge.

All through this mess, she never stopped smiling at me. Her name was Angela, and I could not stop thinking about her. My shift was over; as I was getting ready to leave, the surgeon came in and he was rather angry. He yelled at me and stormed into the administration yelling all kinds of threats about me never practicing medicine again. I was scared.

I waited around to see what would happen and eventually he came out. I tried to talk to him, but he ignored me, walked past me, and left. The administrator then called me in and told me he understood my position, but I was fired.

I went home almost crying; I told the story to my mother, and she told me that all that mattered was that I had done the right thing for the patient, and that is what doctors were supposed to do. She reassured me that there was nothing to worry about and that I would find another job. I went to lie down and try to get some sleep, but I could not stop thinking about the patient and wondered what had happened to her.

I got up after a couple of hours of wondering about her and decided I would find out. I put on a clean white uniform, because I knew it would help me get into Centro Medico and I went off to see her.

I quickly found out that she was in the surgical intensive care unit; so I went up to see her. Needless to say her family was all there. I cautiously approached the unit, and her sister Yolanda approached me and thanked me for suggesting that she be transferred. When she arrived at Centro Medico, she was nearly in shock from blood loss. She told me to call her if I ever needed anything; she actually worked at the IMSS administration. Her brother Guillermo gave me his card also, and she wrote her phone numbers on it.

The patient had been transfused, and they had taken her to surgery for the third time and found no source for the bleeding but a very inflamed large intestine. They performed a colonoscopy and found her intestine to have ulcers from what was eventually diagnosed as shigellosis, an infection of the intestine. She had never had appendicitis from the beginning, and the surgeries had only made the infection worse, allowing the bacteria to ulcerate the bowel. A course of antibiotics would have been the correct treatment; now she had to recover from three surgeries! I wanted to go find the first surgeon and wring his neck.

I asked her family permission to see her, which they granted me. As I walked into the room, there she was cute as ever in spite of her ordeal. The big smile was still there! She had a thermometer in her mouth and could not talk; so I just said that I was glad to see that she was on the road to recovery, and I was just worried and wanted to make sure she was OK.

Then, as I was getting ready to leave, she pulled the thermometer out of her mouth and said, "Please, don't leave," and I never did, literally!

We talked for a while, and I found out she was engaged to be married and that she had a rather large family. She was the youngest. She had two sisters and four brothers. Her older sister was divorced and had a daughter of her own. We had another pleasant conversation, and she made me promise that I would see her again. I got her phone number, which I wrote on her brother's card and left the room smiling. To date I still have that card.

For the next few days I could not stop thinking about her; she eventually got discharged home, and we had some wonderful phone conversations. She told me that the surgeon had told her parents that she had actually gone into shock when she arrived at Centro Medico, but they had been able to give her blood immediately and stabilize her. I had made the right decision! It was nice to hear that I sort of saved her life or at least I thought so.

She also told me that the surgeon had told her father that people who go into shock many times come out of it changed, and she might not be the same person she was before. Then, the surprise news came: she had broken the engagement with her boyfriend!

I visited her at her home several times, and we enjoyed each other's company. She was different from anybody I had met before. She seemed uncomplicated, straightforward, and she was definitely beautiful. We started dating, and her parents allowed her to go out with me alone. I was driving a motorcycle then, so we had a few adventures driving in Mexico City. It was like we knew each other forever.

April came quickly, and the results from the matching program were in. I had matched with the University of Texas in San Antonio's pediatric residency program. I was elated! I had been interviewed over the phone with a Dr. Alexander, and I had really liked what he had to say. I knew I would be happy there. Now I would have to go to San Antonio and find a place to live and buy a car. My motorcycle would not make it to Texas.

Angela and I kept dating and having fun getting to know each other. She played the piano and loved music, just like I did. We seemed to have a connection that I never had before with anyone. The first movie we went to together was *The Way We Were*, starring Robert Redford and Barbara Streisand. We drove to the movies on the motorcycle, swerving in between buses and rushing through Mexico City's traffic. It was fun then, but when I think about it now I don't think I would do it again.

I also visited her at her home and got to know her family better. They were all very nice to me, except one of her brothers who I felt did not like me at first. I had been the reason that she broke her engagement, and her ex-fiancé was a friend of his.

We would also play the piano together. We had just watched *The Sting* and loved the theme. We would play "The Entertainer" together on the piano and had a lot of fun. Even her father would peek into the living room to listen. Eventually, "The Entertainer" became our song; not very romantic but that was just the way we were. No pun intended!

May came and it was getting close to my leaving for San Antonio, so I decided I would ask Angela to marry me. I knew from day one this was going to happen; she was the one, I knew it!

I looked at my savings and decided I could afford a decent ring, so I went downtown Mexico City in search of the perfect ring. I knew she would not like anything fancy, so I looked for a simple diamond ring. Diamonds, though, seemed to be so expensive; I visited many stores and was getting discouraged when I finally found a tiny jewelry store named Arezzo. The owner told me he knew exactly what I wanted. He brought out several rings to show me. All the features I wanted were there: simple and with the right-sized stone. But they were more than I could afford. He asked me how much money I had, and with a big smile he pulled out another ring. It was perfect, and I could afford it! He told me that there was a small defect at the bottom of the diamond, which he showed me under the microscope. I really liked the ring, so I bought it. Nobody ever knew about the defect, till now.

So the big day came: Friday, May 24. I borrowed my parents' car; this was not a day for motorcycling. We went out to eat at the Restaurante Del Lago, a fairly expensive restaurant in Chapultepec Park. We ordered, had dinner, and added dessert, and I could not summon the nerve to ask her. So we finished and went out and got in the car. I did not know what to do, so, eventually, I just parked the car on a street in the middle of Chapultepec Park, turned to her and blurted out, "Would you marry me and go with me to San Antonio?"

She smiled as she always did and said, "*Yes!*"

I gave her the ring but then had to take it back. In Mexico, tradition- ally, my parents would have to ask her parents for her hand in marriage, before she could wear it. It did fit her, and I thought it looked really good on her.

When I went home that night my parents were already in bed. I was so excited; I woke them up and told them the whole story. I asked them if they could go ask for her hand soon since I did not have much time before I had to leave. They told me to set it up and went back to sleep giggling.

Parents asking for a girl's hand in marriage for their son is a very tra- ditional thing in Mexico. We wanted to do it all the right way. Angela and I talked it over, and we arranged for my parents to go over on Tuesday, June 4.

I got dressed up in a suit and tie and drove my parents to Angela's home. After all the appropriate introductions, my father took the lead. He asked her parents for Angela's hand for me. Her father said it was fine if that was what she wanted. Angela said yes; I presented her the ring, and they asked us if we had a date in mind. We said September 6, a Friday, and it was all settled. I was so nervous; it was a great relief when her father offered everybody a drink and proceeded to make a toast to us.

The rest of the evening went on just talking about planning. Traditionally, the bride's parents are responsible for the wedding, and both mothers talked about how to get in touch with each other. I would be gone to San Antonio in less than a month; it was going to be up to all of them to get it all done. Till date, I am not sure if I missed something or was spared it.

Her father wanted a big wedding; it was his baby getting married, so that was how it was going to be. Eventually, I found out that weddings are more for the parents and guests rather than the marrying couple. Don't get me wrong, we loved our wedding, but we would have been happier with just a few friends.

In the second week of June, my father and I drove to San Antonio to find an apartment and a car. I had sold my old jeep and my motorcycle, and I was hoping to find a car of the same value. I did not have much to spend.

We started looking for one-bedroom apartments, but they all seemed too small; I knew Angela would have to have a piano, eventually, and there was no room for one. We eventually came across a two-bedroom third-floor apartment close to the hospital. It was perfect! We did not have any furniture, so we rented it with the essential furniture included for $275 a month with utilities. It seemed like a good deal to me.

I also found a car—a 1972 Toyota Carina, that had done only twelve thousand miles, in great shape, except for two problems: the tires were in bad shape and the owner had lost the trunk key, so it needed to be rekeyed. The price was right: so we bought it, and the people at the lot agreed to hold it till June 26 when I would return.

I was back in Mexico for two weeks; deciding what to pack and what to leave behind were hard choices. I tried to spend as much time with Angela as I could and try to help with ideas for the wedding. There was something I had to have: an antique car to pick us up at the church, so I arranged for it. I also asked my friend Georges, my best friend and singer of the Nowheremen, to be my best man.

Finally, early in the morning of June 26, I left for San Antonio, Texas, looking forward to my pediatric residency. I could not ask for anything more; I had a place to live, a job, and was going to be married to the same person I am still married to after forty-four years. Angela was the surprise of a lifetime.

The course of my life had been set; I did not know at that time that I would never return to Mexico to live. I had no idea where this path was taking me. But something told me it was the right one.

Chapter 7

ON BECOMING A PEDIATRICIAN
THE FIRST YEAR

I arrived in San Antonio in the evening, and I had not even unpacked when I got a phone call from Dr. Alexander asking me if there was any way I could start earlier since one of their residents had to leave early and they needed help. Hesitantly, I said yes.

The next morning, I showed up early at the Robert B. Green Hospital's pediatric department and was quickly introduced to morning report. The crew who had been on call the night before would share with the rest of the house staff interesting cases from the day and night before and the cases that were admitted to the Bexar County Hospital, where inpatient pediatrics was located. It was a lively discussion lead by the attending physicians, Dr. Alexander, Dr. Harold, and the chief resident Dr. Allan, and precisely at eight thirty we would go on a conference call with the residents at Bexar County, who would provide follow up on the admitted patients.

Robert B. Green was only an outpatient and maternity hospital, with adult and pediatric ERs and all the adult and pediatric general and sub-specialty clinics. It housed the obstetrics department, delivery rooms and postpartum rooms, and the NICU (neonatal intensive care unit). Sick newborns were kept there for treatment.

After morning report, Dr. Allan, the chief resident, took me around and showed me were all the services were. Then he took me down to the pediatric ER, which was packed, introduced me to Dr. Martha and Dr. Richard, the two residents working there, and showed me what the work-flow was. He handed me a chart and told me to go to work! I was to ask the other residents if I had any questions. For a moment I had a sinking feeling, but I figured if they could do it, I could it too and started seeing patients.

The pediatric ER was a square; on three sides there were examining rooms and on the fourth side there was an acute treatment room, and the nurses' station. The center was the waiting area. The nurses would screen the patients and place them in the rooms, leaving the charts on the door. We would go from room to room seeing patients, and as we were done we would give the patient the chart and any prescription needed, and he or she would go back to the nurses' station to check out. As long as there were charts on the doors, we would keep going.

When there was a patient who required immediate attention, the nurse would alert one of us, and we would see them right away. If a true emergency came in, the patient would be placed in the treatment room, and one or two residents would be summoned while the third one contin-ued seeing patients.

The pediatric ER had an average of one hundred patients a day; it was a busy place. We saw patients nonstop all day and just took turns for lunch. Check out was at five in the evening when all the clinics were done. The rule was that all the residents and attending physicians would come down to the ER at that time, and everybody saw patients till the waiting room was clear. Then we could go home.

At the end of the day, Dr. Allan came down to the ER and asked me if I could take night call the next day. Again, I reluctantly said yes. I wanted to make a good impression, but deep inside me I was terrified. I went home and stopped by Walmart to buy some linens, plates, and kitchen utensils since I had nothing. I wanted to buy only the essentials since I thought Angela would wish to get what she liked. The apartment was nice, but I had nothing but my books. No television or even a radio. I went to sleep early.

The next day came quickly, at least quicker than I would have liked. I was again assigned to the ER, where I worked all day. One thing about San Antonio was that we saw a lot of patients, so you learned to recognize things quickly and became very efficient. I got to the point that I would walk into a room, and as the mother gave me the history I would examine the child and make a diagnosis, write the chart, and any prescription in just a few minutes.

There was a head nurse in the ER whose first name I do not recall, but everybody called her by her last name: Guevara. She took me under her wing and helped me out a lot on those first few days. Once she came to me and said, "Go to room four; that baby need a needle in his back. I'll be in the treatment room." I went there immediately to find a five-month-old with a 104-degree fever and a stiff neck. She was right. I moved him immediately to the treatment room where Guevara had the spinal tap set ready to go and even the right size gloves already open for me.

She told the mother to wait outside and then positioned the child and held him while I did the spinal tap. The fluid was definitely cloudy—sure sign of meningitis. We started an IV and antibiotics and asked Dr. Martha what to do. She told me to call the resident at "the Hill," which was the nickname for Bexar County Hospital, and arrange for the transfer. So I did; I called the resident, gave the history, and explained what we had done, and everything went smoothly and without a glitch. I could not wait to hear what they would have to say in morning report. It was my first admission as a PL1 (Pediatrics Level One).

But there was still the night to contend with. As the ER was cleared at five, Dr. Allan told me, "You are it for the night, but there are two residents in house; another PL1 in the NICU and a backup PL2, who happened to be Dr. Richard, whom I already knew. So I had somebody to consult if I had any problem.

He showed me the sleep room, which was a ten-by-ten room with a bed and a table, gave me a ticket for my dinner in the cafeteria, and left. I saw a few patients till Guevara told me to go and have dinner since the cafeteria closed at seven, and so I did. By the time I got back there were a few more patients in the waiting room; I saw them and went to bed.

At night, the policy was that if the patient was not a real emergency, they would wait till there were at least four patients before getting the resident up. This was a way to discourage people coming at night just to be seen faster and gave the resident some time to sleep. My night was quiet; I got up once during the night: nothing exciting, just nonemergent simple complaints.

About seven thirty in the morning I ran to the cafeteria, got some coffee, and ran upstairs to Dr. Alexander's conference room where morning report was about to start. I presented my case. The discussion went around which antibiotics I had chosen and why; I defended my position of choosing ampicillin since I thought the most likely bacteria was Group B *Streptococcus*, and it would be sensitive to ampicillin, which would also cover other bacteria. Some felt that it would have been a good idea to include Kanamycin or Gentamycin for added coverage. I had been taught to always use the least amount of antibiotics, so I stood by my decision.

Eight thirty came along and the Hill resident reported that the child was doing well and that the laboratory results definitely showed evidence of meningitis. Then there was a pause and another resident said that the culture was growing gram-positive bacteria consistent with Group B *Strep*. I almost jumped out of my chair! Dr. Alexander just said, "Good job, Jorge." I went back to the ER glowing and puffed up like a turkey in heat!

Later that day, I was called to the pediatric office, and I filled up some forms, including an application for a social security number. They were all required, I was told, if I wanted to get paid. My first check would come in two weeks and then I would get paid every other Thursday. My salary as a PL1 after taxes was about $1,000 a month. I had to pay $275 as my apartment rent, which included utilities, and the rest would have to be enough to pay for food and whatever we needed. This was a big increase from what I was paid in PEMEX, but I also had more responsibilities now. Anyway, I felt I was rich!

I also found out what my schedule would be for my first year. I would spend a total of four months at the Robert B. Green in the ER, the outpatient clinics, and the NICU; four months at the Bexar County Hospital in the inpatient ward and some subspecialties; and four months at the Santa Rosa Children's Hospital for more NICU, private inpatient ward, cardiology, and hematology.

It all seemed fine until I found out the call schedule. PL1s were on call every third or fourth night throughout the year. I thought this was going to be a long hard year, but looking back now, it was one of the best things that ever happened in my training. I saw so many patients and was exposed to many different scenarios. I am thankful I was able to have that experience; sure I was tired sometimes and probably would not have made the best decisions, but I was always supervised by PL2s and PL3s as well as faculty members. I would not trade this experience for anything!

I went ahead and asked for some time off in September since I was getting married on September 6. The best they could do was one week starting September 2 through Monday September 9 when I would have to be back to work. Our honeymoon would have to be a weekend in a half-furnished apartment. How romantic!

For the next four weeks, I stayed working at the pediatric ER; it was a wonderful experience just because of the sheer number of patients we saw every day. The most important thing I learned very quickly was that the nurses knew a lot. Many had been working there for years. Whenever I had a question all I had to do was ask, and the nurses would kindly guide me in the right direction.

One case that always comes to my memory was when a bad asthmatic came into the ER one night. Guevara, who had become my most trusted source of information, was the head nurse. She woke me up and said over the phone, "We have a wheezer that needs help." When I walked into the room, there was a ten-year-old wheezing and having a hard time breathing. I froze, but immediately Guevara said, "How much epinephrine should I give him, Doctor?" She was right; she was politely telling me what to do. I asked for the weight, calculated the dose, and told her. By that time she had already drawn the epinephrine and was ready to give it. Within a few minutes, the child started to improve; in the meantime Guevara had already prepared the IV fluids and asked me if I wanted her to start them while I called for a transfer. Again, I was being guided politely. Then the respiratory therapist (RT) showed up, by magic, and started him on an aerosol. I called, arranged for transport, and eventually he left in an ambulance to the inpatient ward.

When I went back to the chart to write my orders, I saw that Guevara had written them all as verbal orders; all I had to do was sign them. I had just been taught very graciously that I had a lot to learn. Throughout my residency and beyond, I learned so much from experienced nurses; I learn to listen to what they had to say, and I would always be thankful to them. In later years, I tried to pay them back by spending time teaching new nurses what their peers taught me.

During our rotation in the ER we took many cultures on our patients. Every morning one of us was assigned to check cultures. We actually went upstairs to the microbiology lab and personally looked at the culture plates from the night before with the lab technician, and for any positive cultures it was our responsibility to follow up and make sure that those patients were treated appropriately or called back. I learn to recognize most common bacteria at a glance. This was true hands-on personal medicine; I loved each minute of it.

I also enjoyed how much the attending physicians were involved in teaching. Their mere presence in the ER was invaluable. There were there always to answer our questions and teach us a pearl or two! I will never forget the day I saw a patient who had pus coming out of one of his nostrils while the other one was clear. Throat was clear, ears were clear, no fever. I could not figure out what it was, so I went to ask Dr. Alexander, who was there that day. After I presented my case, he looked at me and gave me a pair of ring forceps and told me, "Go take that bean out of that child's nose." He was right! I went back into the room and looked up the nose, and high in the nostril was a decomposing bean! I learned that day that a foreign object is the most common cause of unilateral nasal discharge. Great information!

After my ER rotation I was assigned to the outpatient pediatric clinics. Here we saw in follow up, the patients we admitted after they were discharged. There were also the subspecialty clinics: pulmonary, orthopedics, gastroenterology, cardiology, hematology-oncology, and general pediatrics. At each clinic we would see patients and discuss them with the faculty attending, write a note, and decide on a treatment or disposition.

Our notes were handwritten, in a single chart for each patient. One could read the entire history in a few minutes. The initial note was comprehensive; it included past history, review of systems, physical exam, working diagnosis, and plan. Follow-up notes were relevant and concise. I was able to get a very good idea of a patient's progress in a few minutes. Now, not all handwriting was pretty and easy to read, but we managed. There was nothing electronic!

I loved the clinics, especially the interaction with the faculty; most of them were seasoned clinicians or subspecialists. They also got to know us well and would give us as much freedom as we could handle. Morning report discussions of interesting or unusual patients was something we all loved; it was a time to share our experiences, good or bad, as house officers.

Seeing our own admissions to Bexar County Hospital in follow up was also very rewarding. You got to see the patients you treated acutely in the ER, now doing well and at home. Parents were always very appreciative. I think one of the things that attracted me to pediatrics was dealing with parents; each family has different needs, and you get to learn how to talk to all of them.

There are the very scared ones for whom reassurance is the most important thing to do. I learned that in the worst of circumstances there is always something positive you can find for them. There are also those who demand answers that in many cases do not exist; keeping calm is important in dealing with them. Lastly, there are those parents who are angry, which is their way of coping and always want to find somebody to blame. These are the most difficult for me to deal with. It is very hard to explain that shit happens, and there is nobody to blame. At least, at this point in my career I did not have the new type of parents who evolved in later years: the Internet-knows-it-alls! But I will discuss them in a later chapter.

August went fast, or at least it seemed that way. I had only seen Angela once since I left; I drove down to Laredo to meet her. Her family is from Laredo, and she was having her wedding dress made by one of her aunts.

It is amazing that we met in March, got engaged in June, and we were getting married in September, after having dated only three months. We hardly knew each other!

After being on call the night before on September 2, I packed my bag and got in the car to get to the airport; I was in a hurry and quite nervous. I got in the freeway, and two minutes later I saw blue lights shining in my rearview mirror. I looked down and I realized I was going eighty-five miles an hour! I pulled over, and the policeman came to my window and said, "Sir, you sure are in a hurry! May I see your license and registration?"

I fumbled around trying to find the items and told him, "I am sorry; I am flying today to Mexico to get married, and I was not paying attention."

He laughed and said, "Put everything back and drive on, just slow down and congratulations!" I wish I could remember his name; he sure was the most understanding cop I have ever encountered.

On arrival in Mexico City, Angela and my parents were waiting for me at the airport. It sure was good to see them! Sometimes I wonder if going to San Antonio was the right thing to do rather than staying in Mexico, but in the long run it proved to be an advantage. Angela and I started our married life alone, in a foreign country and with very few friends. We learned to rely on each other for support all the time, and we are still doing it forty-one years later.

We spent the next few days before the wedding taking care of details. I had to get fitted for my tuxedo, and we had to choose the music for the church. We met with the priest to plan on what would go on during the ceremony. We had asked Father Hildebrand, a Benedictine priest from my old high school to officiate. He asked us if we wanted to write our own vows, but we decided to use the usual vows and asked him to let us read our parts. We did not want to memorize anything.

In Mexico it is customary that wedding invitations are delivered personally. Angela and the two mothers had done all of that tedious work already. I never regretted not being there for that. They had spent almost every day in the car going from house to house; in Mexico City's traffic, that was a heroic undertaking!

On September 3, we had our civil marriage. In Mexico, a church wedding is not considered a legal wedding in the eyes of the government, so you still have to get married before a judge. Usually, you pay the judge to come to a place, in our case my parents' house, and in a short ceremony you get legally married, sign the appropriate papers, and get your marriage certificate. This is usually followed by a small celebration with friends and family. Mexicans always find a reason to celebrate.

September 6 arrived, and we were getting married. We had chosen Nuestra Señora del Buen Consejo (Our Lady of Good Counsel), a beautiful modern triangular church, where I used to attend mass as I was growing up. Angela's father had organized a rather big (over five hundred guests) reception at the Club de Leones (Lion's Club). There was to be music by a full orchestra and plenty to eat and drink.

I got up in the morning and walked to the barber's shop around the corner from my home, where I had gone since I was a child, and got a shave and a haircut. Then I went back home and tried to relax a bit; the day went on very fast.

The church wedding was at eight in the evening, my best man was Georges my best friend, who was famous for always being late, and Angela's maid of honor was her best friend Tere. I got into my tuxedo and drove with my parents to the church. My father would not let me drive; he did not think it was safe.

Catholic weddings in Mexico were very traditional; I was not allowed to see Angela until she came into the church. As the ceremony started, the priest came out to greet the entourage and then the procession began. First the flower girls, then the maid of honor and the best man, but Georges was late as usual, so she went in by herself, then my father with Angela's mother, then my mother and I, and after a few minutes of suspense, Angela and her father.

As I waited at the end of the aisle for her father to hand her to me, I could not get over how beautiful she looked. There seemed to be a glow about her; I was speechless. I will never forget that moment. As her father handed her to me, all I could think was how lucky I was to have found her in an unusual sort of way, which some may even consider unethical, but here we were. We were starting a life together, and we had no idea where it was going to take us.

I walked her up to the front of the altar and mass started. Traditional catholic weddings are long: there is a full mass, and the wedding ceremony is performed during the mass. In a little bit of a panic, I kept turning my head back looking for Georges, till finally I saw him take his place. He had the rings!

When the moment came, we read our vows, which father Hildebrand very kindly held up for both of us to read. We said the usual "I Dos," and Georges brought the rings, which were blessed and then we placed them on each other's fingers. Then we were joined by Tere and Georges with a double gold chain. One half was my parents' and the other one was ours. It is a way that parents share their union with their children. We still have our wedding chain and gave my parents back theirs after the ceremony. I think it is a neat tradition.

We chose Father Hildebrand because I knew him well; he had been the first Benedictine priest ordained in Mexico. I went to a school that was run by Benedictine priests from Saint John's Abby in Minnesota, and Father Hildebrand was always very close to my heart. He was always approachable and gave me advice many times during my high-school days. He gave us a beautiful homily. I do not remember much about it anymore, but one sentence stuck forever: "Your wedding lasts only today, but your marriage is for the rest of your lives." Amen!

The ceremony ended and we walked out of the church, and as we were showered with rice, I saw it! The antique car I had always dreamed about was there; we left the church aboard a 1930 Ford Model A sedan. It was one of the highlights of the wedding; everybody cheered as our driver pulled away from the church.

The plan was to arrive at the reception after all the guests had already arrived; in the meantime, we went for a ride, we kissed, and we hugged and enjoyed our antique car ride.

We arrived at the Lions Club and sneaked in through the back door, and they took us upstairs to a waiting room, where we waited for what seemed to be hours. Eventually, we were given the signal to come down. We came down a beautiful set of stairs into the ballroom, with dry ice smoke rolling down the steps. It looked neat, but we could not see the steps, so we walked down rather slowly, which I guess was the desired effect.

As we reached the floor, the orchestra started playing what was supposed to be our song, "The Entertainer," but the conductor had refused to play it because he thought it was not appropriate and that the song should be more romantic. So we danced to "The Way We Were" to please the conductor. "The Way We Were" did have some meaning since it was the theme of the first movie we saw together. After the usual applause, he smiled at us, picked up his baton, and "The Entertainer" began. We loved it; everybody got up and started to dance. We then exchanged partners with parents, brothers, sisters, and friends, till everybody had a chance to dance with each of us. It was the most fun part of the entire wedding!

We sure enjoyed that dance; we were both good dancers, and we had a lot of fun showing off. We got to dance a few more songs and then dinner was announced, and we were escorted to our table overlooking the hall. It was awkward. We felt that we were on display; so we giggled through dinner, cut the cake, and afterward, as required by tradition, we spent the rest of the night shaking hands with all five hundred guests from both families. Most of the time it was people we had not seen in years or did not even know. We did not have much of a chance to dance anymore.

About one o'clock in the morning, as the party was winding down, we said our goodbyes and left. We really did not know what to do with our first night married, because it was one o'clock in the morning, and we had a plane to catch at eight o'clock. So we went home, changed, and spent the night wandering around Mexico City till we ended in a VIPS restaurant for breakfast. We then picked up our bags and headed to the airport. Here, the whole family was gathered to see us off. We hugged everybody, got in the plane, and were happy it was over.

Upon arrival at San Antonio we picked up the car, which I had left at the airport, and went home to our apartment. We sat down and ate some fast food we picked up on the way. I showed Angela around the apartment, we changed, cuddled up in bed, and fell sleep! We were both exhausted!

Sunday morning we got up and went out to buy food and all the things Angela thought we needed. We ate out and came back home to spend our first day putting things away, unpacking, and deciding where to put our things. We argued a little, compromised a lot, and finally settled for the night. This was the extent of our honeymoon; Monday I was back at work!

Back at work, I discovered that all the other residents always pulled this little blue book out of their pockets when they needed information. They told me it was given to them as part of their package when they started. I realized I had not gotten a package, so I went to the pediatric office and found that it was there waiting for me. And there it was: The Harriet Lane Handbook, or "Harriet" as I decided to call it, was the most wonderful thing I had ever seen; it had medication dosages, weight charts, lab values, calculations, and much more. Everything a pediatric resident would ever need. That day my love affair with Harriet started, and I never failed to buy the new edition every three years. The day I retired she was still in my top drawer as she had been for thirty-eight years.

The Harriet Lane Handbook was first published in 1950 by the chief resident at Johns Hopkins Hospital and has been kept up to date since then. For me, it was my best resource, especially since it fitted in my coat pocket. I will always be thankful to Harriet for always providing me with up-to-date information in anything pediatric throughout my career.

My ER/clinics rotation came to an end. It was hard to move on since I was having such a good time, but it was time to learn something new. I was then assigned to the nursery, and the NICU, which was also located at the Robert B. Green Hospital. The obstetrical department occupied most of the second floor, and the nursery and NICU were located on the same floor. There were actually doors from the delivery rooms that opened into the NICU for easy access in case of emergencies.

On my first day, I walked into the nursery, washed my hands, and put a gown on. It was required for the physicians, parents, and visitors to use a gown while in the nursery at all times; the nurses wore scrub uniforms. It felt like a very sterile environment, but on the other hand it gave you some kind of respect for cleanliness. I met my resident Dr. Jack; he was nice and showed me around the NICU and then gave me my patient assignment. I told him I had never seen a neonatal intensive patient before, so he literally took me by the hand and went over every one of my patients with me and reassured me that there would be somebody there every day to help me. I was terrified; I could never have predicted that I would eventually become a neonatologist.

We made rounds and met the attending neonatologist, Dr. Bill, and his fellow, Dr. Primrose. This was a completely new world to me; there were babies that weighed as little as two pounds and many of them on respirators. Every baby was hooked to a monitor, and a nurse technician sat by the bed twenty-four hours. There was a small laboratory next door in which we did the most essential tests in small blood samples. Everything was precise and accounted for on a flow sheet. We knew at a glance all the blood work, how much blood had been used, and when each baby could require a replacement transfusion. It was fantastic!

There were three other PL1s on the same rotation: Lanning and Gea had already been there for two weeks, and Fred and I were the newbies. It was nice to know that I was not alone, but Fred had gone to medical school in the Unites States, so he was familiar with things and so was Lanning. Gea, on the other hand, was from Italy. She was married to an officer stationed at the Lackland Air Force Base, so she was only a couple of weeks ahead of me on learning the system. Our rotations were always different, so we got to work with all the PL1s during our first year. We all became good friends and helped each other.

Newborn medicine was fascinating; I have always been a perfectionist, and this was the field that needed my skill. In these little babies' care there was no room for error. Every day we weighed each baby and calculated the fluid, electrolyte, and caloric needs. When feedings were started, we had to account for each drop and adjust the intravenous fluids. Each change on the respirator had to be calculated to maintain normal blood gas values. Each baby's needs were different, and we had to evaluate each baby often. Dr. Bill used to tell us that every baby had to be evaluated daily, but the smaller the baby the shorter the "days"; so a two-pound baby day was six hours, while a five pounder's may be twenty-four. I loved seeing those tiny babies grow and thrive. This was fun.

We were also in charge of the normal babies born at the Robert B. Green. One of us was in charge of examining and discharging babies every day. There were forty seven hundred deliveries in 1974. That means that there were an average of at least twelve babies born daily, and the same number needed to be discharged. If I learned something on this rotation, it was what a normal baby looked like and what to tell mothers as they were going home with their baby. I had my speech memorized; I also learned all the common questions and how to answer them.

One added skill I learned during my normal nursery rotation was how to perform circumcisions. We circumcised every baby for whom the parents requested it. That was the majority of the males, so we did an average of five or six circumcisions a day. I got so good at it that I could do it with my eyes closed. Some days it was like an assembly line; I would just tell the nurse to line them up! We used to joke about who did the best job; I was nicknamed the "pretty penis maker" by the nurses.

Dr. Bill was a very smart man; he was a self-made neonatologist. There was no certification until 1974, so many academic neonatologists were grandfathered in 1974, and others were required to take an exam. Dr. Bill refused to do it; he had been doing neonatology for many years and felt offended by being asked to pass an exam. Unfortunately, two years later he was asked to leave the faculty because of this. The university required board certification from all their members, and he did not have it. I learned a lot from him. He was a clinician; he always stressed the importance of the physical exam. He used to tell us, "Babies can talk; you just have to learn to listen."

The Robert B. Green Hospital also had a fantastic program that involved the senior ladies in the community. Back in those days, we would not discharge a premature baby until he or she reached five pounds; so we had a large room filled with what we called "growers and feeders." These were babies that were not sick anymore, but were still small, and all they had to do was learn to eat and reach five pounds. These senior ladies would come every morning and were given a free breakfast and a free lunch voucher. Their job was to staff this room under the supervision of a nurse and just sit and feed babies.

The majority of these women were experienced mothers, and the program gave them the chance to feel useful and socialize. When I was free I used to go to this room and sit with them and feed a baby. They taught me many tricks and gave me much advice about feeding babies. Most of all, it was fun to hear their life stories and adventures. Unfortunately, during my third year the program was dissolved because the hospital lawyers did not believe it was safe. We lost one of our most valuable resources for fear of being sued.

After my initial scary impression I learned to love neonatology; working with babies and their parents was very rewarding. The majority of babies did well and went home. Even though there were occasionally some bad stories, over 90 percent of the babies survived. Also, my ability to speak Spanish helped me communicate with our Hispanic mothers; many were illegal immigrants who had crossed the border to have their babies in the United States. It was very reassuring to them to have a Mexican taking care of their babies.

Dr. Primrose, who was doing her fellowship with Dr. Bill, was very helpful; she taught me how to do many procedures. She was from India, and we found many similarities between our cultural backgrounds. She also had a lot of free time and loved to teach. One of the things I learned from her was to always stay cool in emergencies. I loved the adrenaline rush of attending a delivery and performing newborn resuscitation. She always stressed that I was in charge, and if I lost my cool, it was all over. She used to tell me, "You may be scared, but do not show it; stay cool and you will keep everybody cool." I learned from her that I could think quickly and choose a course of action much better if I did not panic.

During my rotation in the nursery I was also exposed to something I had never seen before: babies suffering from withdrawal. The obstetrical department had a very large methadone program for pregnant ladies. Most of them were trying to get off heroin or cocaine and were placed on methadone, and the dose was decreased to a low steady dose. They could not be weaned during pregnancy because the babies would withdraw in utero, and many of them died. Unfortunately, the babies were born addicted and would go through withdrawal in the first few days of life.

It was sad to see these babies go through it; babies would cry inconsolably, sneeze, and be ravenously hungry. Dr. Bill told us there were three ways to handle them; many can be helped just by tight swaddling, giving them a pacifier, and feeding them often; others would be sedated with either phenobarbital or chlorpromazine, and as a last resort they could be treated with tincture of opium and weaned slowly. Unfortunately, this last group would have to stay in the hospital till they were weaned completely, and that might take three to four weeks. His choice was phenobarbital, and so it became mine, I would have to be very meticulous about the dosage to adjust it so that they would be sedated but not too sleepy. It took a lot of observation and work, but I loved it when my dose was perfect and the babies would do well.

My monthlong nursery rotation went very fast, and it was time to move again. This time I was going to be at the Bexar County Hospital inpatient ward. Here we took care of all the patients admitted either directly from a pediatrician or through the ER at Robert B. Green. Very early in the morning we reviewed our patients and gathered all the information available on their progress and then at eight o'clock we would have morning report over the phone with the residents at the Robert B. Green and then we would make official rounds with our attending.

For every new patient we would do a presentation to the group of PL1s, PL2s, PL3s, and the attending physician and discuss the current treatment and any changes. Depending on the attending physician, rounds would last anywhere from an hour to three hours. Then we would go do our work, which usually consisted in writing our note, the orders, and perform any procedures that were needed. There were two groups of residents and two attending physicians who took care of the busy pediatric ward.

I was lucky enough to get Dr. Alexander as the attending physician of my group. He was a lot of fun to work with. He expected us to know every single bit of information about our patients and to present a thorough physical exam. After the first bungled presentation, I learned to be prepared. It was not that he was mean; he just wanted to make sure we knew our patients well and were able to have a clinical working diagnosis before we decided which tests to order or whether we needed to call a subspecialty consultant.

His message always was that you should not order a test unless you know exactly what you were looking for and what results you expected, and for him the only reason to call a consultant was to confirm what you already knew or suspected. He was completely opposed to the shotgun approach to laboratory and X-ray testing. We only ordered what we needed and when we needed it. We had to pay attention to our clinical signs and symptoms; a working diagnosis was always a must.

It was just an extension of what I had been taught in medical school. The history and physical exam come first and testing should be done to help confirm the diagnosis.

I clearly remember when I presented to him a patient who was admitted because of diarrhea and dehydration. When I did my exam I noticed he had a heart murmur. So when I presented the case I said that we needed to consult a cardiologist. He looked at me and asked me what my working diagnosis was. I answered, "Heart murmur." He went ballistic and told me that was not a diagnosis and then proceeded to ask me where the murmur was, how it sounded, how loud it was, and was it in one place only. As I answered his questions I realized that a soft long murmur that radiated to the right chest was likely to be a peripheral pulmonary stenosis murmur. He looked at me and said, "Now, that is a working diagnosis." To make a long story short the cardiology consult confirmed it. Did I really need it? Probably not; it was for reassurance only.

Another thing I learned during my first year in the pediatric inpatient ward was that the PL2s were so knowledgeable. I was impressed. Every time we got a new patient, especially from the Robert B. Green, by the time the admission got to the floor, they were able to give me a very precise list of diagnoses we should consider and what the treatment should be. It was impressive, until I became a PL2 and I realized that they knew the information on the new admission for at least an hour before I did. Most of them went to the pediatric library and read all about it and sure impressed us PL1s.

We were also in charge of the pediatric intensive care unit (PICU); this was again a new world for me. There was technology I had never seen before: monitors that displayed continuous vital signs, including blood pressures, which were measured by transducers. There were beeps and alarms going on unceasingly. It took me a while to get used to all the activity. Like in the NICU things moved fast, and we learned to react quickly. The unit was run by the cardiologists; there were no pediatric intensivists back then, and other subspecialists were involved too, such as the neurologists, nephrologists, endocrinologists, and pediatric oncologists.

As much as I learned to love neonatal intensive care, I soon started to hate PICU. I do not know why it was easy for me to take care of a little baby on a respirator or even loose an immature baby, but I found it very difficult to see an older child depending on a respirator or comprehend why a youngster could die. These were vibrant beautiful children, and they were not supposed to be sick.

I vividly remember a four-year-old who was brought to the unit after he was found in a swimming pool. The EMTs had performed emergency CPR, and he was transported to the PICU. When he arrived he was blue, cold, and not breathing. We intubated him, placing him on a respirator with 100 percent oxygen and started to warm him up; he was lifeless. Dr. J. B. (I never knew his name) told us to not warm him up fast but to keep his temperature around thirty-four degrees for the first twenty-four hours. I had never heard that before, but he felt that hypothermia would provide some protection. Several years later in 2003 this became the accepted treatment.

The child's name was Angel, and he was Hispanic. The mother did not speak any English, so I was commissioned to talk to her and find out any pertinent history. This was one of the hardest things for me to do. Talking to this mother and telling her that her little Angel was very sick and that he may not live was very difficult. I was looking for something positive to say, but there was nothing. The history was unremarkable; he had been healthy until he walked to the neighbor's house and probably fell in the pool. Nobody knew how long he was in the water.

When the neurologist came in and examined him, he was able to see some pupillary reaction. This was good news! We monitored him closely, kept his blood chemistries in shape, and just waited for the best. I was off, but I could not go home. I sat down with the mother, and we both shed some tears. Sometime after midnight, he started to move, and eventually opened his eyes and reached out for his mother. It was so good to see, I cried a little and went home.

The next morning, he was very awake; we pulled his breathing tube out, and he cried. It had been about twenty-four hours since the accident, and he was likely to do well. He remained in the hospital for about a week, because of minor problems, and eventually went home. The mother hugged me on the way out; I cried again.

My inpatient rotation was followed by the worst of my rotations: pediatric oncology. Seeing patients in clinic was not hard, but it was very difficult to see beautiful children diagnosed with cancer go through chemotherapy and little by little lose their hair, their weight, become pale, and many of them eventually die. Chemotherapy was in its very early stage; success rates were very low, and children would stay in the hospital for long periods of time during their treatment, many times receiving many days of intravenous fluids requiring many sticks. All we had was needles; there were no catheters then.

I vividly remember a seven-year-old with leukemia, who was getting chemotherapy. He was getting a high dose of methotrexate an anticancer drug and a few hours later a dose of leucovorin a drug that would rescue his bone marrow. He had very fragile veins; I was called many times to restart his infusion. He would see me come into the room, and even though he knew I had to stick him again, he would always smile. He was so brave; he would actually show me where he thought he had a good vein and never cried. That little guy taught me a lesson in bravery I never forgot; he knew I was doing my job, and I was just trying to help him.

Unfortunately, he never made it home; he had several complications from his chemotherapy and eventually his kidneys shut down. Even though his leukemia seemed better, his little body could not tolerate the treatment. His name was Steven, and even though he was the sweetest cute bald-headed child I have ever met, he was one of the reasons I hated my oncology rotation. I was very happy when it was over.

I spent my last month at the Bexar County Hospital following a multitude of subspecialists during the day and covering the ward at night. I had four one-week long rotations in endocrinology, immunology, nephrology, and genetics. I do not remember much about the first three rotations. Most of the time, we saw patients in the clinics with the attending physician and then rounded on patients who had been admitted to the ward. We were not actually responsible for these patients, but we were consultants. It was a good learning experience since we had one-on-one teaching with the attending.

During my last week I was assigned to genetics. It proved to be the most interesting of all rotations. Dr. Jose, the chief of the division, was my attending, and I spent a lot of time with him. My knowledge of genetics was very little; it was a new and emerging subspecialty, and Dr. Jose made it very interesting. We spent a lot of time talking about chromosomes, which I had learned about in medical school. But this time we looked at actual karyotypes of patients with either extra chromosomes or missing pieces.

Dr. Jose was a walking genetic textbook; he seemed to know everything about every syndrome we encountered; there were no computers to consult back then, just his fantastic memory. We got consulted on a few patients, and I was amazed at how Dr. Jose was always straightforward while explaining to the parents of a child the implications of a chromosome abnormality. His feeling was that chromosomal anomalies were usually untreatable, and it was better for the parents to understand things from the beginning. Some people did not like him because sometimes he seemed coldhearted, but eventually when I was at the receiving end of his explanation I understood what he meant.

February 1975 was gone, and I began my rotations at the Santa Rosa Children's Hospital downtown San Antonio. I had six weeks in the inpatient ward, eight weeks in the NICU, two weeks in pediatric cardiology, and two short rotations on hematology and neurology. After that I would become a PL2!

Santa Rosa Children's Hospital was a private catholic hospital run by the Sisters of Charity of the Incarnate Word. The children's hospital had opened in 1959 as the region's first hospital solely dedicated to the care of children, and it was part of the pediatric residency training program. For me it was a little bit of a new experience in the sense that the sisters were very conscious of waste, and everything needed to be accounted for, and supplies were used more judiciously than in the county hospitals. It was a different environment; we were now dealing with private patients.

My inpatient rotation was uneventful; the pace was more relaxed than in Bexar County, and pretty much all the patients were private patients so there were many attending physicians since the pediatricians oversaw their own patients. We would admit the patients, work them up, discuss our diagnosis and plan with the pediatrician, and write the history and the orders. If any procedure needed to be done, we would do it usually supervised by the PL2. Most patients were simple and easy to treat. The six weeks went by quickly and were somewhat boring. My next rotation was pediatric cardiology.

I really was not very interested in pediatric cardiology, but my attending, Dr. Colette, made it so interesting that I learned to love the specialty. She was not only a shrewd clinician, but she had dedicated her entire life to the care of children. She would follow her patients closely, and if any of her patients required surgery, she would attend the surgeries and stay with her patients until they were stable. Many times she would sit at the bedside overnight. She always made sure the nurses understood her orders precisely, and she did not tolerate even miniscule mistakes. I learned from her never to leave the bedside until I knew that the nurse had read and understood each and every order.

Dr. Colette was very inspiring; we would spend a lot of time in her office just talking. She had been one of the founders of the faculty at the medical school, and she knew a lot about its history. She also had an intimate knowledge of cardiovascular physiology; we spent many hours just talking about how the heart worked and what each wave in the EKG meant. Whenever she had to do a cardiac catheterization, she would explain everything in detail; it was fascinating to see her work. But most importantly, I was captivated by the relationship she had with her patients. They followed her instructions without hesitation, and in turn she was there any time they needed her.

She had another cardiologist who worked with her; her name was Dr. Betty, and she definitely looked like a "Betty." She always wore her hair puffed up, very old fashioned, and dressed like in the '50s. But she was sweet and always willing to teach. Her interest was in cardiac echocardiography, which I had been exposed to in medical school. Her machine was much more advanced; the screen was bigger, and she could actually stop the image and do actual measurements. She was able to follow the course of patent ductus arteriosus closure, estimate the size of the left atrium and left ventricle, and estimate valve gradients. This was still all experimental, but it was cutting edge. Throughout my career, I was always drawn to experiment with new technologies.

My next rotation was in the NICU, another eye-opening experience. Santa Rosa's NICU was a lot different from that of the Robert B. Green; Santa Rosa was the regional nursery; babies were flown in from all the surrounding hospitals. The number of acutely ill babies was much larger, and the spectrum of diseases much more varied. I thought I had died and gone to heaven! The director of the unit was Dr. David, and he also had a fellow Dr. Remedios.

Usually, the PL2 would be notified of a baby in an outside hospital in need of transport, and he would arrange for a military helicopter to take two nurses to go pick the baby up. With two air force Bases and one army base in San Antonio, there was never a problem finding transport. Occasionally, if the PL2 felt that it was necessary to have a doctor on board, the PL1 got to take a trip. I absolutely loved transports; I would even volunteer if there was a chance. It was fun to arrive at the referring hospital, stabilize the babies, and then bring them to the NICU.

Things did not always go well. There was one instance where I was sent to pick up a baby at a small community hospital. In spite of our insisting that they keep the baby at the hospital, they insisted at meeting us at the airport. Unfortunately, they did not own a transport incubator, so when we arrived they were waiting for us with the baby in a cardboard box wrapped up in blankets. Fortunately, the weather was warm enough to keep the baby warm; I had to stabilize the baby at the helipad before we could leave. Not an ideal situation.

The other instance was a bit more exciting; we were asked to go pick up a pair of small twins. Dr. Gea and I were assigned to go. It was a beautiful day; we arrived to the hospital with two transport incubators and two nurses. Both babies appeared stable; we started IVs on both, placed them on oxygen, and started our way back. Midflight, Gea looked at me with panic on her face; her baby was not breathing. He needed to be intubated. She started to do it, but the vibration of the helicopter was too much. She looked at the pilot and yelled, "We got to land!" Immediately, the pilot looked around and very quickly landed in an open field and turned the engine off. As things settled, Gea placed the tube in the baby's trachea and after securing it told the pilot "*Go!*" We arrived at the hospital uneventfully. I will always remember how cool Gea was throughout the whole thing. Later she told me that she was shaking as badly as the helicopter; we just could not see it.

I loved my eight weeks in the NICU at Santa Rosa as much as I did at the Robert B Green; there was something about these little guys that attracted me. My compulsive personality was perfect for the care they required. I was also reminded again and again of how important it was to listen to the nurses; they were the ones who knew the babies, and it always paid off to listen to their advice.

My last two rotations were short one-week rotations. The first one was hematology, where I met Dr. Howard, who was the director of education at Santa Rosa. It was fun because he was a fun person to work with, always jolly and in a good mood. We spent most of the week doing consults and examining blood smears. The last rotation was neurology with Dr. John. He was young and likeable, but I was glad it was only a week long. I always hated neurology; it seemed to me that most of the patients we saw did not have good outcomes.

Chapter 8

FROM RESIDENT TO CHIEF, AND A NEW BABY

It was July of 1975; I was now a PL2 resident. It meant less work, fewer calls, but more responsibility. Now I had to be there for the PL1s as the PL2s had been there for me during the past year. I was not sure I was up to the task, but I was willing to give it my best shot.

I will have to say that I admire Angela's attitude throughout those first years; her family was far away, and we could not afford many long-distance phone calls. She had virtually no friends in San Antonio, and I was not home a lot, but she was there for me every day. To make things worse, her English was not very good, and she did not know how to drive.

When we first arrived, we were given money instead of wedding presents by many people. We used most of it on buying a piano. We found an old Everett upright and had it delivered to our third-floor apartment. The delivery people were not very happy about bringing it up the stairs.

Angela had been playing the piano all her life, and it provided something to do when I was not home. She was a classically trained pianist, and she would spend many hours practicing. We did not know it at the time, but this 1931 piano was one of Everett's original dyna tension scale pianos and had ivory keys. Many years later when we traded it in for a baby grand, we got more than we had paid for it.

One of the most exciting things about being a PL2 was that I would have more time to be home. Throughout my first year I had been on call pretty much every third night; Angela did not see much of me, and when I was home I was so tired that I would fall sleep often. I am sure I was not much fun to be around. Now, I would be on call every fourth or fifth night, and I would have a few more weekends off. More importantly, my salary would go up to $1,200 a month.

That was a year of many changes. The first one was a new apartment. We figured out that there were cheaper apartments close to Bexar County, so in July when our lease was up, we moved to a one-bedroom apartment that was only $200 a month with utilities. We would save seventy-five dollars a month! We did not have to worry much about moving furniture since we did not own any; everything we had was rented. We only had to pay to move the piano; we bought a mattress/box spring and a small yellow table with four chairs. We figured we could survive with these till we could afford more.

We enjoyed our new apartment; it was only second floor and had a fairly spacious living room and dining area. Eventually, we made shelves with concrete blocks and wood planks and bought a sleeper sofa so that we could have visitors. Finally, we visited the unpainted furniture store and bought a dresser and two night tables. We had furniture we could really call ours.

As a PL2 I now had the responsibility of teaching the PL1s and supervising their work. If I ran into trouble there were still PL3s and the chief resident to back me up. When July started and I assumed my new role, I realized how much I had learned the year before, and little by little my confidence grew. Not only I had seen a lot of patients in my first year, but through rounds and conferences I had also acquired more knowledge than I realized. I also had more time to read and investigate new and interesting cases. I felt I could contribute more to my patients' care than I did as a PL1.

I started my rotation at the Bexar County Hospital in my second year. In my new role I always had advance notice of admissions coming from the Green. I had time to research the library and learn as much as I could about the possible differential diagnosis and impress my PL1s. But I also had more responsibility to make sure everything was done correctly and my PL1 was ready to tackle morning report. I felt that how the PL1s did reflected on me, and I wanted to make sure they were well prepared. I also knew the attending physicians' likes and dislikes and passed on pointers to the PL1s on how to present their cases.

We had several good PL1s that year, some very strong and knowledgeable but a couple who were somewhat weak. I learned to recognize their strengths and weaknesses and help them through. I really enjoyed teaching, but I enjoyed it more when my trainees did well. I also realized that there was a lot to be learned if one intends to teach others and that learning is a changing affair, in medicine; when you think you know everything about a disease, something new comes up. So staying up to date is very important.

One case reminded me of that fact during my last month at Bexar County. I was called by a pediatrician, who was sending an eleven-year-old girl, a known juvenile diabetic who had developed a cold and fever. In spite of staying on her diet and insulin, she had developed very high blood glucose and was not able to control it at home. I alerted the pediatric ICU nurses and notified Dr. Scott my PL1. When she arrived we got her history: her name was Leslie; she had a cold and had been taking aspirin every four hours for her fever, and her mother told us she had drunk several sodas because she was very thirsty and had eaten a couple of candy bars. Her physical exam was unremarkable except that she was sleepy and had an unusual red rash on her palms and feet. Her blood work came back. As expected her blood sugar was very high; there were ketones in her urine, and the rest was pretty unremarkable.

I sat down with Scott, and we calculated the insulin required to bring her sugar down, started IV fluids, and developed a plan to continue to monitor her blood sugar closely. I loved these calculations!; I knew that we would have her blood sugar under control slowly over the next few hours. Everything looked fine, so I went to the call room to read more about diabetic ketoacidosis.

About six hours later, Scott called me and told me he was worried because even though her blood glucose was improving she had become less responsive. I went down and reviewed all the blood work. Glucose was almost normal; everything else was normal, but her level of consciousness had changed. She was combative and not responding to commands. Her parents were there and terrified. I called my PL3, and he called the attending physician; within an hour we had everybody there.

Leslie continued to deteriorate, became totally unresponsive, and quit breathing; we intubated her and place her on a ventilator. We checked blood gases and found her to be somewhat acidotic. We called the endocrinologist; she could not understand why she was not improving, but she told us to check the blood ammonia level and that she would be on her way. By the time she arrived the ammonia value was back; it was five times normal.

She walked into the room, looked at her, and the blood work and said, "She has Reye's syndrome." Nobody in the room knew what that was.

We asked her, "How do we treat it?" She said, "There is no treatment; keep doing what you are doing and pray." I was devastated.

I could not give up; I sat by her bedside and tried to monitor and treat what we could. Unfortunately, Leslie continued to worsen, and within forty-eight hours she expired. Her parents were angry; they kept asking me how come it happened. I had no answers.

After that episode, I learned everything there was to be learned about Reye's syndrome. Unfortunately, there was not much information available. It was not until 1979 that is was found to be associated with the administration of Aspirin in children and guidelines for management were published. If we had only known that back then we may have been able to save Leslie.

My four months at Bexar County were finished; my next four months were spent at the Robert B. Green, which I loved. I would be back in the clinics for the first two months and then in the NICU. As usual the clinics were fun; I loved to work with Drs. Alexander and Harold. It seemed like every day I would learn something new, and in the pediatric ER there was never a dull day. Now, I was the one to tell the PL1, "Go get that bean out of that child's nose!"

I think one of the advantages of the San Antonio training program was that we got to see so many patients that we learned to recognize the common things and pick those that were different and required more attention. We spent a lot of time in the hospital, but we learned a lot, too.

January came quickly, and I was back in the NICU. This time I got to help the PL1s and teach them all I had learned. There were things that I enjoyed doing, so I used to volunteer to go the delivery room and teach the PL1s how to properly resuscitate. I also loved working with the NICU nurses. I think there is a natural selection in nursing because NICU nurses seem to be different; they understand babies, and that is not something you learn.

Little did I know that my life was going to change forever.

I came home from work one afternoon, and Angela seemed a little worried. She had always been very irregular in her periods, but this time it had just gone too long. Her last period was on November 16, and we were now in January. She also had not been feeling very well, especially in the mornings. We both looked at each other, and I said well, maybe we should get a pregnancy test. There were no home tests in 1976, so I had to take her urine sample to the hospital in the morning to be tested.

I took the urine first thing in the morning to the laboratory at the Robert B. Green. I knew most of the techs, so they promised to let me know as soon as it was ready. I went back to the NICU to make rounds. Within an hour I heard them paging me overhead to the lab; I ran upstairs. The technician saw me and said, "Dr. Rojas, you are pregnant!"

I said, "What?"

She repeated the same thing; all of a sudden I realized I was going to be a father. I ran though the nursery and told everybody. Grabbed the phone and called Angela; she was also excited, but I think she already knew I was just confirming it for her.

Then I ran around the hospital telling everybody I knew. When I got to Dr. Alexander's office he laughed at me and said, "Go home, Jorge. See you in the morning." I didn't argue and took off.

When I got home we kissed and hugged and decided to go out and celebrate. We went to Mi Tierra the best Mexican restaurant, we could afford. We had a great time; we were both on cloud nine. I am not sure how much we slept that night, but it wasn't much. We made many plans! But the morning came, and I was back at work and investigating which obstetrician we should get to see Angela.

I wanted to keep things as close as possible, so I asked about the obstetrical faculty members. Everybody recommended Dr. Bob; he was an Asian American young faculty member. I made an appointment, and within a week we went to see him. He sat down with us for about thirty minutes and went over what he expected from us and what were to expect from him. It was a detailed, reassuring conversation. We needed that! He examined Angela and told us she was about eleven weeks, and everything looked fine and that he would plan on seeing us in a month.

The rest of my rotation in the NICU was uneventful; I spent a lot of time learning the workings of the blood gas machine. We had our own machine in the nursery, so we could use very small samples and use the same blood to do other simple tests. This was cutting-edge technology! I was so attracted to all new things, and neonatology was the place to be. Most babies had respiratory problems, and we were using the first baby respirators called the Baby Birds; I wanted to know how they worked and what they did.

On my last week at the Robert B. Green NICU I was fortunate to meet one of the doctors who designed the Baby Bird; Dr. Bill invited Dr. Bob D. from the military to come and give us a lecture. He did just what I was craving for; he showed us how the ventilator was built, how it worked, and what it did for the baby. This was a lecture I would remember forever.

My last four months were back at Santa Rosa Children's Hospital; the inpatient ward was usually relaxed. I enjoyed the leisure time talking to the nurses and the sisters. It was a different environment than the county hospitals. Even though the sisters always made you aware of anything wasteful, they never turned down any of our requests for whatever we felt was necessary to take care of a patient. It used to be said that Sister Mary Margaret's motto was "Do what's right for the patient, and we'll take care of the details in the morning."

Santa Rosa's ward rotations were always interesting; we got more exposure to the private pediatricians and not just the university faculty, and so we got exposed to new things about "the real world" that the pediatricians dealt with every day. Being a resident was exciting; patients came to the hospital, and we took care of them and sent them back to their pediatricians. I got invited a couple of times to pediatric offices as an observer; it was a little disappointing to me that the life of the regular pediatrician was somehow uninspiring. They saw many patients every day, and probably 90 percent of them were either normal checkups or colds. I was not sure I was cut out for that.

Then it was again time to start my rotation in the NICU, and everything changed! There was always something new going on: calls to the delivery room, procedures, adjusting respirators, running blood gases, so many things! I loved teaching the other residents; I was lucky to have had a lot of hands-on experience during my medical school clinical years, and things like minor surgeries were right up my ally. Whenever we had a baby that suffered a cut during a C-section, I was so excited to teach others how to do invisible stitches; my babies never had a scar.

I became very close to Dr. David and the fellow Dr. Remedios, whom we called Remi. I learned a lot from them; we had long discussions about respirator management and how to troubleshoot respirators. Neonatology was such a young field; there was so much to be discovered. New studies were published every month. Remi had a project on using umbilical artery cutdowns when there was no arterial access on a baby. It was not unusual to get babies transported in when the local physician had bungled the umbilical artery, and doing a cutdown was the only way to get an arterial catheter. She taught me the technic, which I used and improved throughout my career. I never realized how lucky I was; very few neonatologists had surgical skills.

Angela was doing well; we had been to the obstetrician four times. She was now twenty-eight weeks, and everything seemed fine. Her pregnancy seemed to be progressing well, but at the last visit, Dr. Bob told us that the baby was somewhat smaller than he expected at twenty-eight weeks. He thought that with Angela being so irregular, there was a chance her dates could be wrong. He did not seem to be very concerned, so we tried not to worry. She was feeling up to sewing and preparing an old-fashioned crib for the baby. She did an amazing job, with lots of lace and ribbon. Fit for the prince who was coming!

Even as a PL2, I was still spending a lot of time in the hospital. That would be the story of my whole life. On Angela's birthday, I had given her a puppy, a cute female toy poodle, which we named Windy after the weather on the day we pick her up. She was at least a little bit of company, and taking care of her gave Angela some other things to do.

We were now in June, and the end of my second year of pediatrics was fast approaching. One afternoon I got a phone call from Dr. Harry, one of our current chief residents. He asked me to come to the pediatric department office the next morning at 8:00 a.m. before I went to the NICU; he had already asked the on-call resident to cover for me. He would not discuss anything else over the phone, so I went home worried that I had done something wrong. I did not get much sleep that night.

In the morning, I got up early and arrived at the pediatric office. Lanning and Sharon, two other PL2s, were there. Nobody seemed to know what was going on. The secretary told us that Dr. Phillip, the chairman of pediatrics, was ready to see us. We went into his office; he asked us to sit down and then told us that the faculty and the PL3s had decided that we were the best three candidates to become chief residents in the coming academic year. First, I was relieved; second, I was speechless. This was something I was not expecting, but it was exciting. We were to have our usual rotations through the three hospitals, but would only be on call once a week, and our salary would be $1,600 dollars a month. I knew Angela would be thrilled!

Being chief residents we would be responsible for making schedules for the PL1s and PL2s and for organizing lectures at each location as we felt it was needed. We were also responsible for presenting grand rounds once during the year at our convenience. They expected us to either have a research project of our own or work in one with a faculty member.

I left the office on cloud nine and floated down the interstate to Santa Rosa. The first thing I did as I arrived was pick up the phone and call Angela; she was excited for me and happy to hear about fewer calls and more money. Life was good!

When I got home that evening, we thought about the baby coming and the salary increase, and we decided to talk to the apartment management and see if we could move to a two-bedroom apartment so that we could have a nursery for the baby. They were nice to us, and within a week we had a brand new apartment. For the third time in three years! We still did not have a lot of furniture, so moving was easy. Several of our friends helped, and we even moved the piano without a glitch.

Angela now had a nursery to work on and I a new and exciting job as chief, and both had a baby to look forward to.

July came and I assumed my new role as chief resident; I was happy that my first four months would be as chief resident at the Robert B. Green; not only did I love to be close to the NICU, but I also found the outpatient clinics fun. I had been working on the schedules since I knew I would be chief resident, and by July 1, I was ready. I did not know the new PL1s who were starting, so I made sure that they were always one of the better PL2s or PL3 in house, especially for the first couple of months. I discussed my schedule with Dr. Alexander, and he liked it. I was thrilled.

I scheduled myself in any place I knew they would need extra help, and I made sure that every day I checked in the pediatric ER and the NICU to make sure everybody was doing well. Again, I found out that the nurses were my best source of information. They would always tell me who needed extra help, and I tried very hard to solve problems. I felt that how everybody did was a reflection on me. I was glad to have Dr. Alexander and Dr. Harold always available; I learned a lot from them on how to handle problems.

Being a chief resident was the first time I had to learn to deal with people; I had a hard time at the beginning, but with the advice of Dr. Alexander, I learned that the most important things in dealing with people are to do the following: first, be a listener; even if it takes time always listen to what people have to say, and second, show interest; people always appreciate when you care about them. Two policies I have followed always.

By the end of July, Angela's pregnancy was now thirty-six weeks, but her uterus was only thirty-three weeks' size. Dr. Bob seemed worried, but he kept telling us that maybe her dates were wrong. I was also growing concerned, but I tried not to show it and remained positive. There was not much I could do. We had been attending Lamaze classes, and we kept ourselves busy practicing what we were taught. Angela wanted to have a natural delivery with no drugs, and I was ready to be her coach.

Working at the Robert B. Green was always fun and a great learning experience. It was always busy, whether you were in clinics or the pediatric ER. The sheer number of patients we saw every day was a learning experience; we learned to spot what needed our immediate attention and what could wait. The nursery and the NICU were also the same; with four hundred babies born every month, we had an opportunity to examine lots of normal babies and to see an amazing number of abnormalities. Interpreting laboratory values and X-rays became an easy task. Sure we spent a lot of time in the hospital and worked many hours, but we learned a lot just by being there.

We were now in the middle of August; Angela's due date was rapidly approaching, and Dr. Bob seemed to be getting more and more concerned with the baby's growth. She was now thirty-nine weeks, just one week short of term, and the baby was still measuring only thirty-four weeks. The gap seemed to be growing; even if the dates were wrong it did not seem to be a logical explanation anymore. Deep inside me I was very worried, but I refrained from saying anything; I did not want to worry Angela any more than she already was.

Two more weeks went by, and, finally, on September 5, Angela went into labor. It was the night of Jerry Lewis Labor Day Telethon, so we watched it for a while at home until her contractions were consistent and then we drove down to the Robert B. Green. Angela was admitted to a labor room. The 1976 telethon was perhaps the most memorable one in the MDA's history, highlighted by the emotional reunion of Jerry and his former partner Dean Martin. We watched it all through the night while she labored for fourteen hours. Just as a side note, the 1976 telethon was the most watched, drawing more than eighty-five million viewers, according to A. C. Nielsen.

The morning came. September 6, our second wedding anniversary. Labor was progressing slowly, but during the last couple of hours the fetal heart rate monitor started to show some decelerations that seemed to be getting deeper with time. Finally at about eleven o'clock in the morning, the heart rate went down, and it would not come back up. Dr. Bob was called; he examined Angela and said she was completely dilated, and he could deliver the baby with forceps. All went so fast, it was like a bad dream. He put the forceps and pulled hard; in a few seconds the baby was out. The pediatric team was there; I saw them working with the baby and then moving it to the NICU. I never heard him cry; we were scared, but we just hugged and waited for the neonatologist to come and talk to us. Dr. Bill was out of town so Dr. Primrose had called Dr. David from Santa Rosa to come and see the baby.

We stayed in the delivery room for a long time while Dr. Bob stitched Angela, who had suffered a third-degree tear. Finally, Dr. Dave came in and told us that the baby was breathing fine on just a small amount of oxygen, but he did have some anomalies and wanted me to go with him to the NICU. I reassured Angela and went with him.

Jorge Luis, that was his name, was lying on a warmer in an oxygen hood. He was small, only weighed four pounds even, and he seemed to be breathing easy. Dr. David pointed out to me that he had bilateral clubbed feet, and his fingers overlapped. But the rest seemed fine to him. He did not look fine to me; his head was small, his hips were stiff, and he had a very week cry. I knew immediately there was more going on.

I went back to Angela; she had been moved to a room. I explained to her what I had learned. I tried to be positive, but I am sure she knew things were very wrong. Dr. Robert, whom we had met during my first two years of residency, was to be our pediatrician. He came in and told us that he was afraid the baby had a chromosomal disorder, but he was not sure which; so he had asked Dr. Jose, the geneticist, to look at him.

That same afternoon after what seemed to be a very long time, Dr. Jose, the geneticist, came into the room. In his own straightforward way he told us, "The baby has trisomy 18; there is no cure." I was in shock. Angela was confused; she had not heard of the condition before. Dr. Jose explained that he would send blood to confirm the diagnosis, but he was one hundred percent sure. He explained that the majority of babies with trisomy 18 died within the first year of life, and only less than 1 percent survived beyond. He left; we looked at each other, and we did not have much to say. We just cried.

In the evening, the nurses told us the baby was doing well and brought him to us in the room. They gave Angela a bottle, but Jorge Luis did not seem to be interested in drinking. We spent some time with him, and they took him back to the NICU. It was late, and we were exhausted. Angela needed some rest and sleep, and I needed to go home, check on the dog, and clean up. We decided I better stay home and get some sleep, too.

The next morning I returned to the hospital early. I found Angela feeding the baby with one of the nurses helping her to feed. She seemed in good spirits. Father George, a catholic priest, stopped and offered to baptize the baby; since the prognosis was so uncertain we agreed, and he was officially named Jorge Luis.

Dr. Robert also stopped by, and we decided that we would not do any kind of treatment or diagnostic tests since the prognosis was so poor. He talked to the nurses in the NICU and placed a sign on Jorge Luis's bed that read, "Please notify ME about every aspect of this patient's condition. NOTHING is to be done on this patient without my consent." He definitely wanted to be in charge, and that was fine with us.

The rest of the day was an amazing parade of people who wanted to show their love; many nurses from the three hospitals came by, as well as residents and many faculty members. The phone never stopped ringing. We were overwhelmed by the outpouring of affection we were shown. We had so many flowers, there was no more place to put them in the room, so we started giving them away to the nurses.

They kept on bringing Jorge Luis to the room every four hours for Angela to feed; he would take maybe a half an ounce and did not seem interested in having any more. We had agreed to not do any treatments, but I could see that Angela was having a hard time not being able to provide enough milk. Breastfeeding was out of the question. We discussed it with Dr. Robert, but he was hoping things would improve with time.

The next morning, Dr. Bob said Angela was ready to go home, if Dr. Robert was ready to discharge Jorge Luis. He came by later on, and we agreed to go home. He would check with us in a couple of days at home. He gave us his office and home numbers and encouraged us to call if we had any questions. Dr. Harold also came by and told us our apartment was on his way to the hospital, and he would check on us in the morning.

We packed up, gave away most of the flowers, and headed home.

Before we left, we wrote a letter to the staff and handed it to the charge nurse as we left:

To the
Robert B. Green Hospital

We have a little Angel! He was born at the Robert B. Green Hospital, September 6, 1976, and he was lucky.
He came into a world where all he saw was love, care, and understanding. Everybody welcomed him; but he soon found out that his perfect soul was not in a perfect body, and he will have to go back.
He is happy and thankful; he found this world full of caring people. Doctors, nurses, clerks, and friends taught him only good things and surrounded him with love. He wants to try again. He wants to come back, and maybe next time he will get a perfect body and will not have to leave.
God Bless you all at the Robert B. Green for making him be the LUCKIEST of angels!

Sincerely,
Jorge & Angela
Rojas

Chapter 9
A HARD GOOD-BYE AND THE END OF RESIDENCY

We settled back home with Jorge Luis. Angela continued to try to feed him every four hours around the clock, but he would hardly take one half ounce each time. When Dr. Harold came by to check on us in the morning, he told me that Dr. Alexander had told him that I did not have to go to work the rest of the week.

Angela told him that even though we had agreed to not do anything to keep Jorge Luis alive, she felt that feedings was something she had to give him. It was hard for her to think he was not getting enough. He told her that we should discuss that with our pediatrician Dr. Robert and decide what the best way to proceed was. He was there as a friend, not as a doctor.

That same afternoon, Dr. Robert showed up. He had the results of the chromosome analysis; it was definitely trisomy 18. He told us that he felt our plan of doing only basic care was the right way to go. Angela told him she could not continue with giving him just a little milk; she wanted to make sure he was getting enough. Since he hardly ever cried she could not tell whether he was hungry. He told us that he needed at least an ounce every three hours. Angela knew she could not do that, so the only alternative was to tube feed him. I told Dr. Robert that I would pick up some tubes at the hospital and teach her how to do it.

I drove to the hospital and picked up some feeding tubes and headed home. The first time, I put the tube in, and we fed him an ounce of milk. He went to sleep right away. Three hours later, I let her put the tube in; she was scared but did it without a problem. We checked for leftover milk; there was none, so we gave him another ounce. We kept this up every three hours around the clock. The strength that Angela showed was amazing; she got better and better every time, and eventually she even joked about "spaghetti time"!

I was angry; I did not know at whom or what. I felt we did not deserve this punishment, and many times I even blamed God. When I look at the pictures of myself and my son, there is not a smile on any of them. On the other hand, Angela seemed to become more accepting every day. I could see she began to actually enjoy motherhood while I secretly considered myself a failure as a father.

Dr. Harold stopped by almost every day that week; it was nice to have somebody to talk to, for both of us. But it was time for me to go back to work, and he promised he would continue to come by and check on Angela and Jorge Luis when I was on call. For me going back to work was an escape; I had read everything known about trisomy 18, and I knew things would just get worse. Going back to work was selfish, but I needed to get my head straight, and feeling useful was better than staying at home and feeling helpless.

I worried about the hospital bill for Angela and Jorge Luis. We were given Blue Cross and Blue Shield (BCBS) insurance by the university, and the hospital had sent all the charges to them. We finally got a letter at home from BCBS: the total hospital charges were $975, but all the charges were covered, and we would not be charged by the hospital. I was so relieved; I had no idea what the future held and what kind of needs Jorge Luis would have, so this was a big weight lifted off my shoulders. We never got a bill from any of the doctors; we were extended professional courtesy.

In 1976, BCBS was a not-for-profit organization and was tax exempt. It had been created in 1929 to administer health plans for many companies, across the United States, which by paying monthly fees guaranteed health coverage to their employees. In 1994, BCBS changed to allow its licensees to be for-profit corporations and in many states became publicly traded. In 2010, BCBS nearly doubled its income. BCBS went from being accountable to the companies it covered to being accountable to its shareholders. This was the beginning of health insurance becoming a business instead of a service.

As I returned to work, things got worse for me. Everybody seemed to either ask questions I did not want to answer or ignore the situation. Both things bothered me; I just went about by my business doing my job until one day Dr. Alexander called me to his office and asked me what was wrong. First I said nothing was wrong, but he knew me well, and eventually I opened up and told him how guilty, angry, and helpless I felt. He did not say much; he just listened, but at the end I felt so much better. He told me, "Go home and tell Angela what you just told me." I thanked him and went home.

He was right; I got home, and we talked. Angela felt the same way I did, but like me she had been reluctant to talk about it because she was afraid of hurting me. We decided we would just take care of Jorge Luis and enjoy him as long as he was with us.

Over the next couple of weeks, Jorge Luis started to look better; I guess nutrition was making a difference. His cry was louder, and he started to react to our voices and make faces. We even saw a couple of smiles; we were finally beginning to enjoy him. We started taking him out when we went shopping, and invariably we would get questions about his size. We would just say that he was a premature and avoid any more comments. Angela always made sure his hands and feet were covered.

Dr. Robert would stop from time to time to see us and told us we did not have to go and see him in his office; he would continue to make home visits since we had decided not to do immunizations. We did have an appointment with Dr. Jose at the Birth Defects Evaluation Center in November. Jorge Luis was now two months old.

When we met with Dr. Jose, he was surprised; Jorge Luis was now almost eight pounds. He was alert, he smiled, and his exam besides his anomalies was normal. We only had one question for him: Why do babies with trisomy 18 die? We could not understand why when Jorge Luis looked healthy, he continued to say he would not live long.

He sat down with us in his office and explained that, in the majority of cases, babies with trisomy 18 die suddenly and without an obvious reason: "It is like something just turns the switch off." He felt we should be prepared for the fact that there was nothing we could do to change the outcome. Planning ahead with our pediatrician would be wise, rather than having him end up in the ER with people who did not know him. He was a wise man; we will always be thankful for his sincerity.

Over the next couple of weeks Angela's mother and my parents came to visit and spend some time with their grandchild. It was nice to have them around for a few days and even brag about the things that Jorge Luis had accomplished, but deep inside me I felt like I had failed to give them the grandchild they were expecting. Both grandmothers did not seem to care; they treated him like he was normal. My father on the other hand, never picked him up and kept his distance; maybe he did not want to get attached. I will never know, but it made me angry.

I had finished my rotation at the Robert B. Green and was now back at Santa Rosa Children's Hospital. Things were going well; I spent as much time I could in the nursery with Drs. David and Remi in the NICU, but I continued to supervise the PL1s and PL2s in the ward and jumped into every newborn transport I could get myself assigned to. I loved transports! It was a time when you were in charge, and even though you always had access to the attending, you got to call the shots!

This was the last year of my residency; it was time to make a decision on what would be the next step in my career. Most of the PL3s were joining pediatric practices, but a few of us wanted to do a subspecialty. I was one hundred percent sure I wanted to be a neonatologist, but I had no idea which programs I should look into.

I talked to Dr. David. He thought I should go to a place where my Spanish would be helpful; he suggested looking into programs in Texas or Florida. Dr. Bill had left the program because he was under a lot of pressure to take the certification exam for neonatology. He actually left pediatrics and joined the radiology program as a resident. He recommended that I go to a strong academic program; if I wanted to join a faculty someday I needed to get experience on research.

Dr. Alexander had no doubts about where I should go. To Vanderbilt! It was not only because it was his alma mater but also because he knew I would enjoy being in a research-oriented program, and in his book there was nobody better than Dr. Mildred. She was one of the pioneers of neo-natology; she had a fantastic research program, and Vanderbilt was a pre-mier academic program. He could also give her a call and give me an awesome recommendation. I told him I would think about it.

At about the same time, we had Dr. Eduardo, the Director of the University of Miami program, as a guest speaker for Grand Rounds. I had the opportunity to show him around the Santa Rosa NICU and talk to him about his program. He was interested in me because I could speak Spanish, and by the end of the day he offered me a fellowship position. I told him also that I would think about it.

It was December 1, and I had the afternoon off; when I got home I noticed that Jorge Luis's color was not as good as always, and he seemed sleepy. Angela had noted the same thing. We sat down in the living room to watch television, and he was sitting in his infant seat. He seemed to be sleeping, but his color got worse. I got close to him; he was not breathing. We hugged each other, and we both knew this was the end; I could not feel a pulse either.

As we had planned, we called Dr. Robert, and he told us he was on his way. When he arrived, he looked at Jorge Luis and confirmed what we already knew. He told us he had to make two phone calls, one to the police and the other one to the funeral home we had chosen. In the meantime, I covered Jorge Luis with a blanket. Angela did not want me to, but he was not looking good, and I insisted. We just sat on the couch and hugged.

Then things started to happen, and one of the worst days of my life began. The bell rang and I went to answer it. As I opened the door, a big guy pushed the door open and me aside, and as he identified himself as a police detective, he demanded to see the dead baby. Dr. Robert talked to him and tried to explain that the baby had a fatal condition, and this was expected; he did not seem to listen and came to me and started asking the same questions. Finally, he uncovered the baby and realized he was not a normal baby; he mumbled a few more things, asked Dr. Robert if he was signing the death certificate, and left.

A few minutes later the funeral director Mr. Pope came in; he was very proper and considerate. He asked us if we knew what we wanted to do. We had no idea; so he told us we could just come to the funeral home in the morning and decide. He asked us to go to the bedroom while he took the baby away. He had a large suitcase with him. We went into the bedroom, and I could not help but look out of the window and see him leave with the large suitcase. I knew he had taken Jorge Luis in it.

Dr. Robert told us he was gone. He gave us a hug; we thanked him and he left. We sat down in silence for a while; we cried and eventually went to bed.

In the morning we got up and drove over to the funeral home where we met with Mr. Pope. He was very kind and seemed to know what we needed. He told us that they had a package for babies, which would include a small plot in an area called Babyland, a fiberglass casket, and a small graveside ceremony all for $347. The plot would be purchased in perpetuity. We did not expect anybody to come, so it was fine and something we could afford; so we agreed. We were advised to go home and return the next day. He would give us some time with the baby in a chapel and then we would move to the grave site. We agreed, signed the papers, and went back home.

It was hard to be home without Jorge Luis; the house seemed empty, and we did not talk too much. The phone rang all day. Many family and friends from Mexico called. It seemed like we told the same story a million times. Finally, we just decided not to answer it anymore; we both felt very tired and just wanted to go to bed.

We had been told to be at the funeral home at ten in the morning; as we arrived the funeral director took us to a small chapel where Jorge

Luis was lying in his white casket. We both felt he did not even look like himself; his face was full of makeup, and it just was not him. We both gave him a kiss; he felt cold, like a rubber doll. It was reality finally sinking in. He was dead.

Mr. Pope gave us about an hour in the chapel by ourselves and then he said it was time to go to the graveside. He asked us to wait outside while he sealed the casket. Then he came out with the casket in his arms and told us to follow him. Babyland was just a few steps from the funeral home. He carried Jorge Luis in his arms all the way.

As we arrived at the grave site we were surprised! There were a lot of people there. We did not expect anybody, since our families were far away, but there were nurses, doctors, faculty members, secretaries, and friends. We were overwhelmed; we never realized that he had touched so many lives and that so many people cared about us. It was a very humbling experience. There were so many flowers! We never expected this, but we will never forget it.

Things went quickly then; Mr. Pope had asked a Catholic priest from a nearby church to say a few words and then everybody came and gave us hugs and offered condolences. Neither Angela nor I can recall much of it. We only remember that after everybody left Mr. Pope told us to go home. The casket was still above ground; I guess we were expecting to see him buried, but he told us that was not customary. We left and were told the memorial we had picked would take a couple of weeks to be erected, and he would let us know.

I don't remember much about the days that followed. I felt numb and did not do a lot of talking. I kept on thinking of what my mother had told me over the phone: "God always does things for a reason; someday you will understand." Looking back, after forty years, what I learned then has helped me understand what parents go though not only when they lose a baby but also when that baby is not perfect. We had to grieve twice: first for the perfect baby we did not have and then for the one we finally had accepted and that had died.

Over the following weeks, I found myself crying many times and trying to appear strong but quickly found out that Angela was the strong one; she kept our marriage together and was always there when I needed her. She helped me through Christmas, which turned out to be a very sad and difficult time. I eventually went back to work, but she stayed home alone. I never heard her complain, but I know it must have been very hard.

Everybody was wonderful at work, not many people asked questions, but they were always there when I needed to talk. As I went back to work, there were only two things on my mind: as a chief resident I was expected to give Grand Rounds and even though I had been able to postpone it, my time was coming, and I had to make a decision on where I wanted to go for my fellowship. I had been offered a position at Miami, but Dr. Alexander insisted I should look into Vanderbilt before making a decision.

I talked to Dr. Mildred over the phone, and she seemed very positive. She told me I could either become a clinical fellow or a research fellow. A clinical fellow spent 100 percent of the time in the NICU, while research fellows can spend as much as nine months every year working on research projects in the sheep lab. This was very intriguing to me since I had never been exposed to research, so I decided to visit their program before making a decision.

Angela and I drove to Nashville. It was one thousand miles, but we decided to do it in one day. We left at five in the morning and arrived in Nashville at seven at night. In the morning I drove to Vanderbilt and visited with Dr. Bob; Dr. Mildred was out of town. He showed me the NICU and then left me with Dr. Ross, a third-year clinical fellow. He was very positive about the opportunity to see a great variety of cases because of the regionalization program, which gave Vanderbilt a large referral area. All the transports were done by the fellows, so there was an opportunity for lots of hands-on experience.

Then he took me to see the "van" as they called it; its real name was the Angel One. It was a newborn intensive care unit on wheels. This was an amazing vehicle; it had everything you needed to take care of a baby. Even a blood gas machine; it was state of the art! I also got to meet some of the personnel who ran the van. Lee, one of the drivers, and Kim and

Odessa, a couple of the transport nurses. They all seemed very nice and encouraging.

He took me to lunch where we met Dr. Dan, a PhD who did the entire computer work for the program; he was fascinating. Then Dr. Ross took me to the sheep lab, where I met with Dr. Beth, a third-year research fellow. She showed me around and introduced me to Dr. Hakan, who was the director of the lab. It was so interesting; the lab was in the middle of the hospital building, and the sheep were kept right in the courtyard. He went over some of the research projects that were going on and plans for the future. It was fascinating! I was sold!

In the afternoon, we met with a lady from one of the local banks. Ross had suggested that we have her show us the city and places to live. She took us to different areas of the city, and we stopped and gathered information on some apartments. She also volunteered to open an account for us in her bank. Even though we had not made a decision yet, she opened the account with only a ten-dollar deposit. She wanted our business! Interestingly enough, forty years later we still have our account in the same bank.

In the evening, we decided to explore the city on our own; Dr. Bob suggested we check the Percy Warner Park. Even though it was the middle of January and it was cold, it looked like a beautiful park. We drove around, and we took one of the small roads into it. We had never seen an icy road in our lives; as we were going down a hill, the road was covered with ice. The car started to slide, and it did not matter what I did, we were going down. The more I applied the brake the worse it got. Finally, I just let the brake go and let the car roll freely, and eventually I was able to control the car. We finally stopped at the bottom of the hill and slowly drove out of the park. It was scary, but luckily it was the only bad experience we had in Nashville.

We went back to the hotel and the next morning drove back to San Antonio. I think I spent the entire trip trying to convince Angela that Vanderbilt was where I wanted to go; for her it was going farther away from home and to a city that had virtually no Spanish-speaking population. For me it was an exciting proposition; doing research was intriguing, and I really wanted to work in the "van." As usual she was game for anything I wanted to do. The next morning I called back Dr. Bob and told him I had decided to go to Vanderbilt.

I also called Dr. Eduardo in Miami; he was not happy. He insisted I reconsider, but I had made my decision. Dr. Alexander was happy; he was sure I would do well. Above all, I was convinced that Vanderbilt was where I wanted to go.

My Grand Rounds were approaching fast, and I was at a loss for what to do. I was supposed to work with Dr. Rajam, one of the new neonatologists. She was very nice and asked me if I wanted to do a neonatal topic. I said yes, but I had no idea what to do. She asked me, "What is the most important thing you have learned about babies in the last three years?" I told her my hardest lesson was not as a doctor but as a parent with the birth and death of my firstborn. She looked at me and said, "There you have it: grief from the point of view of a parent and a physician is something you can share with all of us."

That was a lot of food for thought! I went to the library and immersed myself on every piece of literature I could find on grief and grieving. Then I ran across Elisabeth Kübler-Ross and her book *On Death and Dying*. The more I read, the more I understood what I was going through and how much some people around me had helped me. This was my first research project; I shared all this information with Angela and asked her if she would join me at Grand Rounds and talk about the mother's side. She was reluctant at first but eventually she agreed to do it.

I spent all my time off preparing my talk. I went back to Dr. Rajam for advice many times, and by the time April 6 came, we were ready. Dr. Rajam introduced me with very kind words and explained how we had come up with the topic and then it was my turn. I was nervous, but after the first few minutes, I settled down and gave my presentation. Angela followed me and talked about the mother's point of view; she was awesome! I closed and answered a few questions. This was my first adventure in public speaking since high school; I loved it!

This was also the beginning of a growing interest in death, dying, and grief; and it helped me help many parents throughout my career. Here are a few excerpts from my talk, which I have kept in my file forever:

"In our modern society, the death of an infant is an uncommon event. In the past there was a ritualized pattern of mourning behavior after a death. However, over the past fifty years death has moved from home to the hospital. The sequence of grieving practices for the family has broken down. As a result, the traditions that have been developed over the past hundreds of years which ensure a normal mourning reaction have been lost.

"It is important to realize that in most parents affectional ties to their babies begin even before pregnancy starts and accelerates with the development of fetal movement. The purchase of clothes, a crib, and the choosing of a name help both parents to develop these affectional ties. Parents develop attachment to this "baby image," which essentially is already an individual. The mourning after a stillborn or malformed infant is similar to that of an older family member. Emotional ties exist long before the baby's birth.

"From the physician's point of view, I believe that we have a responsibility to fulfill three goals: 1) To help the parents accept the loss and make it real, 2) to ensure that a normal grief reaction is allowed to happen with both parents, and 3) to meet the individual needs of a specific family.

"It is important to realize that the care of the parents does not stop with the hospital discharge and that following up with the family throughout the entire process is important. Many families may still have questions months after the death of the infant."

Angela followed me and discussed the mother's point of view:

"The more Jorge and I shared, the more we learned about each other. We learned how hard it can be for two people to try to meet each other's needs. Sometimes we were angry at each other; other times we were able to share our feelings.

"During the months following the death of Jorge Luis, the support we needed came from our doctors, who continued to talk to us, and our friends. Sharing our feelings with others seemed to lessen the burden."

And I finished as follows:

"Even though I had placed much emphasis on what we say, I want to make a point that when visiting with grieving parents, much of the time is spent listening, often with long periods of silence or crying. This sitting and listening is difficult for a busy nurse or physician, but it is time well spent.

"Grieving does not stop with the parents; nursery personnel grieve too. Quoting from Kennel and Klaus: 'In a true sense the NICU is like an extended family, with the director and head nurse playing an important role in maintaining high morale.'"

I took those words to heart the rest of my life.

After Grand Rounds were done, I just went back to my chief resident job and started planning our next move to Nashville, when we got unexpected news. Angela was pregnant again! We really did not expect this, but it was a welcome though scary thing.

We made our appointment to see Dr. Bob again. He was excited for us and told us that this time we would have a normal baby. Chances of a repeat trisomy 18 were less than one in ten thousand. He also told us that in a few weeks we could do an amniocentesis and be sure. It sounded like a good plan to us.

I was now at the end of my residency; I was technically a pediatrician. Medicine was so far what I had expected. I had prepared myself to be a good clinician, to listen carefully and examine thoroughly, to make careful decisions based on this information, and above all, to "do no harm."

Making money was never my primary objective but to be the best doctor I could be with the tools I was given.

So far, medicine was the career I dreamed of, which followed the Hippocratic oath: "I solemnly swear that I will contemplate human life as sacred, from conception to death and that I will make it the purpose of my life." Medicine was a service to others, just what I had seen my father and brother do. I was enjoying every minute. This was what I signed up for! I only had one more step to go through; I must take my pediatric boards: a long multiple-choice exam like I had never taken before.

The exam was hard: so many questions, and it appeared to be in so little time. I had never done something like that: questions with one answer, questions with multiple right answers, and many true and false questions. I did very poorly; I spent more time trying to understand the questions than answering them. By the end of the exam, I had answered only three-fourths of the questions. I knew I would not pass.

Several weeks later I got my results: a horrible nonpassing 62 percent, the worst score of my entire life. I was devastated. I went to see Dr. Alexander, who was always there for me. I was in tears. He told me he was certain I knew my pediatrics. I just did not know how to take that type of test. So he referred me to a course at the university that taught how to approach multiple-choice exams. I took the course. Several months later, when I was in Nashville, I retook the exam. I passed it with 91 percent of correct answers. Dr. Alexander was correct, as usual; I will always be thankful for all that he did for me.

Angela was now fifteen weeks, and Dr. Bob recommended that we do an ultrasound and if everything looked fine we could proceed with the amniocentesis.

The ultrasound was normal; Angela had been feeling the baby move for a while now. We saw the baby during the study, and the technician thought it looked normal. We asked her not to tell us the sex; we did not want to know. But there was a problem; Angela had an anterior placenta, an amniocentesis might be dangerous.

We met with Dr. Bob and discussed it at length. He told us he could try to do it, but there was a risk for the baby. It was a low risk, but we could lose the pregnancy. This time it was different; Angela felt the baby move early, and there was a lot more movement than the first time. Size was normal, and the ultrasound did not pick up any abnormalities. We decided to take our chances and not do the amniocentesis.

He recommended that we see Dr. Frank at Vanderbilt; he was a perinatologist, which was a brand new subspecialty. He would make the referral and send the records to him.

He also felt that it would be good for us to deliver at a new hospital and be surrounded by new people. He was so positive that we left the office feeling that refusing the amniocentesis was the right decision.

Now it was time to move on; we had already arranged for an apartment, and we rented a big U-Haul truck. With the help of a couple of friends, we loaded it and set it so that we could pull our car behind it. We planned to do the trip to Nashville in two days since the truck had a governor that did not allow us to go faster than 55 mph, and I did not want to put Angela in any stressful situation.

We then made the rounds and said our goodbyes to all our friends in San Antonio. On June 30, we packed up our bags, our two dogs, and one parakeet; got on the road and headed for Tennessee.

The day before we left, I got a large envelope from my mother. It contained a handwritten poem she had composed about Jorge Luis. I will share that here both in Spanish and English. Unfortunately, my translation does not do justice to the original Spanish version.

My mother always amazed me in that she could see beauty in everything. This was her way to show us that even though the birth and death of Jorge Luis had brought us a lot of pain, there was also beautiful side!

"El Ángel *Que Se Fue. . .*"	"*The Angel that left. . .*"
Nos llegó un angelito que no perdió sus alas,	We got a little angel, who did not lose his wings;
Se le olvido dejarlas en el cielo al partir;	He forgot to leave them in heaven at his birth.
Y llegó a nuestro mundo, con su eterna mirada	And he came to our world, with his eyes always fixed
Puesta siempre el cielo de límpido zafir.	On the clear blue color of heaven above.
Era lindo, era tierno como una flor del cielo,	He was nice; he was tender like a flower from heaven,
Añoraba los rayos de la luz sideral;	But he missed the rays of the cosmic light.
No encontraba en el mundo el fulgor de su estrella	He could not find the glare of his stars in this world,
Con la que, entre las nubes, le gustaba jugar.	With what, among the clouds, he used to play.
Tal vez quiso quedarse al saber que era amado,	He wanted to stay when he learned he was loved,
Al sentir que unos brazos le daban su calor;	After he felt the warmth of his parent's arms.
Pero aquellas alitas que en sus hombros estaban	But those little wings attached to his shoulders
Se movían presurosas para tornar a Dios.	Hurriedly moved to return him to God.
Y así, por fin un día las inquietas alitas	And so, finally one day those restless wings
Emprendieron el vuelo al reino del Señor,	Flew him back to the Kingdom of the Lord,
Y nuestro ángel pequeño se alejó de esta vida	And our little angel departed from this life
Al llamado imperioso del cielo que dejó.	At the imperative call of the heaven he left.

Los otros angelitos lo esperaban gozosos,
Jugando entre las nubes con rayitos de sol;
Y él se marchó contento, sabiendo que fue hermoso
Conocer de este mundo solo un inmenso amor.

The other little angels welcome him joyfully,
Playing among the clouds and the rays of the sun,
And he left happy, knowing that it had been a joy
To learn there was great love in this world.

For my grandson Jorge Luis.
Born on the September 6, 1976,
Gone to heaven on December 1 of
the same year.

Marta B. de Rojas

Chapter 10
NEONATOLOGY, RESEARCH AND A NEW BABY

We arrived in Nashville on June 30, late in the evening. The apartment we had rented was a two-bedroom, two-story town house. We unhooked the car and backed up the trailer as close to the door as possible, and I started unloading. It became dark quickly, and we were exhausted. Unfortunately, we learned yet another lesson on what not to do. Never load your bed first! We could not get to the bed or mattress. We did have some blankets, so we lay them down on the floor and went to sleep. We will always remember our first night in Nashville!

Early in the morning we got up and Angela whipped up a quick breakfast and coffee, and I went back to unload the furniture. Within minutes, a couple of neighbors showed up and offered to help; I guess a pregnant lady and her husband looked pretty pitiful trying to unload the U-Haul truck. They told Angela to sit down and just direct. Before we knew it, there were six people helping, and in one hour everything was in the apartment. I have never been so thankful to have these wonderful neighbors we had never met before.

We had the long weekend to unpack; Monday was July 4, and I did not have to report till the fifth. We still did not have a lot of furniture, but we felt the apartment looked good. It is always exciting to be at home even if it is a brand new empty one!

We took the U-Haul truck back to a gas station about a mile from the apartment, and, unfortunately, had to walk back since we could not get a ride back and Angela was not driving yet. The walk back was actually very nice; there were not very many houses, so we walked partly through the woods. Little did we know that we were about to learn about Tennessee ticks! By the time we got home we were full of them! One more lesson learned.

On Tuesday morning, I was at work bright and early. Dr. Mildred was still out of town. One of the secretaries in the office, by the name of Melanie, took me to get my ID card and my parking sticker and delivered me to Dr. Ross in the NICU. He was the fellow on call, and they wanted me to learn how to handle transports. I joined him on rounds with Dr. Bob.

As we went around seeing each patient with the team of residents and interns, I started to see that there were some differences in the approach to therapy from what I was used to. Later on in life, I learned that there is only one right way to do things, and it is different for every institution. But I was eager to learn the reasons behind everything, so I asked a lot of questions. The residents did not seem to appreciate this; I was slowing rounds.

About noon, a call came in from a town called Lewisburg. I had no idea where this was, but Ross explained to me that it was a very small community hospital and that the referring doctor was a family practitioner. He explained to me that in many of these small towns the physicians were not very experienced in the care of sick newborns so one should always advise them on simple things to do while the van arrived, like give oxygen to keep the baby pink, make sure he or she was kept warm in an incubator, and do simple blood tests such as a PCV.

I thought I had learned all the initials in medicine, but I had no idea what a PCV was. So not to appear too ignorant I asked the transport nurse, Kim, what it was. She told me that it was packed cell volume or what the rest of the world called a hematocrit. This was just the beginning of learning a whole new set of initials that seemed to be only used at Vanderbilt.

We jumped into the van, and Lee the driver explained to me that it was a well-equipped vehicle but not very fast. It was equipped with a telephone so that we could be in contact with the referring physician in case he needed help. When we were a few miles before the hospital, Ross went back and calibrated the blood gas machine so that it would be ready on our arrival.

As we arrived, Kim and Lee unloaded the transport incubator; it had a monitor, oxygen, air, and even a respirator. We went into the hospital, where we found the baby in the nursery in an oxygen hood at 40 percent. Ross took me with him to talk to the mother, while Kim got the baby ready to transport. He was very good reassuring the mother while obtaining a history; the baby was six weeks early, and his lungs were probably not mature yet. He got her to sign a permission to transfer the baby, and we went back to the nursery where Kim had the baby ready to go.

We moved the baby inside the van; Kim moved him to the open warmer. Ross placed an umbilical artery line, ran a set of blood gases, and adjusted the oxygen. In a few minutes, we were back on the road to Vanderbilt. I was amazed at how smooth everything went and how well equipped the van was. I had been used to rushed helicopter transports, and this was very different. It was like bringing the NICU to the baby and then leisurely driving back.

On arrival, Ross transferred the care of the baby to the admitting resident and told me that that was the extent of his responsibility. The fellows did all the transports, but their involvement in the care at the NICU was minimal. Once the residents took over, the fellow was relieved of all responsibility. That seemed odd to me, but as time went by I realized that the residents had complete control over patient care. The attending physicians and the fellows would discuss the plan during rounds, but it was up to the residents to follow it. This bothered me, and eventually when I became an attending, trying to change this was one of the things that got me in trouble.

Over the next few days, I met the other fellows; we were all in a large office all together. There were seven of us: Ross, Beth, Docia, Susan, Robert, Asha, and me. Ross and Beth were third-year fellows, but everybody else was starting. Docia and Susan were clinical fellows and the rest, including me, were research fellows. We shared the same office, a large room with seven desks. We all got along well; it was nice not to be on call except every seventh night!

I had not still met Dr. Mildred; she had been out since I arrived. Dr. Alexander had told me so many stories about her that I was really looking forward to meeting her. I never thought our first encounter would be such that it would define our relationship forever.

I was on my first day on call, and a call came in early in the morning. It was from Murray, Kentucky, a town about 120 miles away. The baby was a term baby who was desperately ill and in need of immediate attention. The van would take about two and a half hours to get there, and I thought that was too long. I asked Odessa the transport nurse if there was a way to get there sooner. She told me on occasion they would get a helicopter from Fort Campbell to take them if necessary.

I was used to helicopter trips; I called the fort and arranged for a helicopter to meet us at the HCA helipad, just two blocks away and take us there. The trip was uneventful; we were there in thirty-five minutes. The baby had an infection; she needed to be placed on a ventilator and given antibiotics and blood pressure support. We stabilized her and flew back to Nashville. It all went well, and I transferred the baby to the residents upon arrival. I was proud of what we have done; I felt we saved the baby's life.

As I was leaving the NICU, this short old woman started yelling at me about not using the van and getting a helicopter. I did not take this yelling well; I calmly told her that I did it because I felt that we needed to get there quicker than the two and a half hours the van would have taken. I had made a judgment call, and I felt it was the right one for that patient. She stopped yelling, looked at me, and said, "OK, but the van should be the vehicle of choice."

I agreed and started to walk away, when Odessa came running to me and said, "I guess you just met Dr. Mildred." I almost died!

But Dr. Mildred extended her hand and said, "Welcome to our program, George."

I don't know if our relationship through the years would have been different if I had known who she was and not stood up for myself; but from that point on she always respected my opinion and never, in the six years I was at Vanderbilt, raised her voice at me. Through those years I learned to respect her and appreciate how she pushed everybody around her to do their best. She was one of my best teachers.

Dr. Mildred was an amazing clinician and teacher. She was not an attending physician in the NICU anymore, but she would do teaching rounds on Wednesdays. I tried not to ever miss one of them.

The residents would pick an interesting patient and the PL1 would present the history to her, and she would lead a discussion on the appropriate type of care. She was very hard on the residents; she would ask for minuscule details on the history and physical exam. She was an exceptional clinician. She believed that 90 percent of diagnosis can be made by a careful history and physical exam. The lab and X-rays were just to confirm it. She was from the same school of thought I had been exposed to in San Antonio; I thoroughly enjoyed her discussions.

The residents hated her; she was demanding, and she expected to be looked in the eye while presenting a history. She did not like excuses; if you did not know something it was better to say, "I don't know" than try to make something up. But she got the best out of people; she would push you hard, but you knew that if you tried your best she would know it.

I think there were only two groups of people at Vanderbilt: those who hated her and those who understood her and loved her. I fell in the second group right away. She was not only a great motivator, but she read a lot and knew a lot. Her knowledge of newborn physiology was amazing! She had actually done a lot of the landmark studies herself, studies that could never be repeated under current human research regulations. She had trained the nurses in the NICU personally, and it did not matter how anybody felt about her; everybody respected her.

There were only three neonatology attending physicians in the NICU: Dr. Mildred, Dr. Bob, and Dr. Hakan. Dr. Bob was the director of the NICU and a fantastic clinical researcher; he was very interested in the

PDA or patent ductus arteriosus, a vessel that normally closes, but in some premature babies it stays open and frequently sends them into congestive heart failure. He was also interested in new technology, and his right hand was a PhD by the name of Dr. Dan. He was a computer wizard! He is responsible for me ever getting into computers.

My second month was spent being oriented to the research lab. Dr. Hakan was the director of the lab, which was known as the sheep lab. The lab was situated in the first floor in a building just behind the hospital, and it was equipped with a multitude of large recorders, which could be tailored to be used for heart rate, respirations, and any pressure or volume measurement; it was state of the art! It had an operating table, an anesthesia machine, and anything needed to perform major surgery.

Rao and Cookie were the staff of the sheep lab. Rao was a veterinarian from India who took care of the animals and anything that was needed in the lab. He could not get a veterinary license because of his foreign training; so this was a perfect job for him. He was the sweetest man I have ever met. Cookie was a nurse; she had traded humans for animals, but she was a fantastic animal nurse. She could do everything from starting IVs or giving anesthesia to being a surgical assistant. They both were the life of the lab; it was always a pleasure to see them in the mornings.

Most of the research was done on newborn or premature lambs, a model that was developed by Dr. Mildred several years before. Premature lambs develop a disease very close to what is called hyaline membrane disease in human newborns, which makes them ideal for study. Ewes with perfectly timed pregnancies were brought in and the lambs delivered at precise time to study them.

What I did not know was how the ewes came to the hospital and how they were dated. But I learned soon enough.

Dr. Hakan told us one afternoon that they were bringing pregnant ewes one afternoon after all the clinic appointments were done. He told us to change into scrubs and take two carts to the street in front of the hospital. A farmer pulled up in a truck hauling a trailer full of ewes. There must have been at least twenty of them. We brought the carts to the back of the trailer, and the farmer helped us load two ewes on each cart. There was a lot of kicking and fighting, but we manage to fill both carts. Then Dr. Hakan said, "Let's go to X-ray." I had no idea what was going on, but we rolled the carts with the sheep through the clinic corridor into the X-ray department and then all hell broke loose! We had to take each ewe out of the cart and lift it onto the X-ray table for an X-ray to be done to time the pregnancy. By the time the first four were done, we were all as stinky as the sheep, and many of us got plenty of bruises from kicks.

We took the ones that had the correct dating to the courtyard and the ones that did not went back to the trailer, and we repeated this operation nine more times. By the end of the evening, we had X-rayed nineteen ewes, and eleven were kept. During the return trip, one of the ewes got away and ran up the street. There we were in our surgical scrubs chasing a sheep down the street; people driving by would stop, and we heard many laughs at our expense.

To be honest it was a kind of a gruesome experience, but I was so excited about the research that I did not mind doing it. By the time I got home all I wanted was to take a shower! Angela agreed wholeheartedly as I walked through the door.

The sheep lab was one of the best experiences of my life. I learned the intricacies of animal research, from taking care of these beautiful animals to sacrificing them to obtain data to help human babies. As an animal lover this was not easy for me to do, but I understood what needed to be done.

Of the research fellows, Dr. Robert was the one I seemed to work with the most. We were both interested in the pulmonary system, and he knew a lot of mathematics and physics, which I benefited from. We became good friends; he was also a good clinician, so we enjoyed discussing patients and treatment options while we were on the clinical service.

In the sheep lab we were studying the effects of a toxin derived from a streptococcus that attacks babies. This was new and exciting research. We would use newborn lambs that had been instrumented while they were still in the uterus. Then we would deliver them by C-section and study the effects of the toxin on their pulmonary function immediately after birth and at different times after. Sometimes these experiments lasted several days. We kept the lamb on a respirator and treated it as we would a baby in the NICU. We spent many long nights "nursing" our lambs.

But there was a lot of data that needed to be collected and analyzed, so we made good use of the time taking care of these lambs. Unfortunately, at the end of each experiment, the lamb had to be euthanized and an autopsy done so that we could take samples for Dr. Mildred to study the pathologic changes in the lungs. This part I never enjoyed.

We did have an unfortunate episode happen to Dr. Robert and me. One night we were in the lab with our lamb on a respirator and stable. Usually, we would take turns going to the cafeteria for dinner, but this time we decided that the lamb was stable and sedated so it would be OK for both of us to leave for a few minutes and grab something to eat. We did not spend a long time away, but upon return Dr. Robert went in to look at the lamb while I washed my hands.

Suddenly I heard *"Yitgadal v'yitkadash sh'mei raba!"* Dr. Robert, who was Jewish, was reciting a mourner's prayer in Yiddish. Even though it was on a respirator, the lamb must have had a cardiac arrest; it was definitely death, and there was nothing we could do to change that. We sat quietly for a while and then we decided to call Dr. Hakan and let him know; he was not happy. We had a hard time explaining what happened, since we were not there, but all we could do was ask for forgiveness.

I loved every minute I spent in the sheep lab. I learned so much about how to measure things and then how to collect the information and analyze it. I spent countless hours with long paper sheets full of numbers, adding them and calculating statistics. Dr. Robert and I spent hours discussing what the data meant and what would be the best statistical test to apply.

Rao and Cookie were an amazing source of information, and they were wonderful people to work with. Whenever we stayed overnight with a lamb, Rao would show up in the morning with a coke and a bear claw pastry for each of us. He used to call it "survival kit"; the caffeine and the calories were always welcome.

Cookie was a joy to be around, always smiling and making sure everything was in place and in working order. She knew the ins and outs of all the machines, and she made sure we always had the supplies we needed. As my experience had been with nurses though the years, even in the sheep lab she was the one with the knowledge.

Dr. Hakan on the other hand was somewhat difficult to deal with. He had a very dry personality; I rarely saw him smile. If things did not go perfectly, he always looked for somebody to blame. We used to joke about it. One day we decided that we would pick a person to be the culprit of the day so that way everybody else could relax. So we would write it on the top of the blackboard, and when something went wrong we all blamed that person. It began as a joke but eventually made him think twice every time he wanted to blame somebody.

Every Friday afternoon, we would have a research meeting with Dr. Mildred. Each of us would present what we were doing and how the data was shaping up and then she would ask questions and suggest changes that she felt needed to be done; she was always challenging. Both the lab and clinical research were discussed. For some reason she always seemed to pick on Dr. Hakan and the female fellows. On many occasions I saw Dr. Docia or Dr. Susan leave the room teary eyed. Somehow, she never raised her voice at me.

It was October by now, and I had been at Vanderbilt for almost four months. I was spending a lot of time in the hospital, whether it was on call, doing transports, or in the sheep lab. Angela's pregnancy was approaching what we thought was term or forty weeks gestation, and all was well. The baby was growing normally, and Dr. Frank was very reassuring. He told us we would wait for her to go into labor on her own.

Two weeks later she was still not going into labor, but she was already five centimeters dilated, and because of the previous pregnancy history Dr. Frank decided it was time to deliver. We came in the hospital on November 8 at nine o'clock in the morning and about ten Pitocin was started. Within a few minutes Angela started to have contractions, and they were pretty strong. I tried to get her to focus and breathe as we were taught in our prenatal class with Jorge Luis, but she was going strong and fast. By about eleven she told me she wanted to push; I knew it was too soon, but I asked the nurse to check her.

The nurse came in the room and skeptically agreed to check her. As soon as she did, she panicked and asked the desk over the intercom to page Dr. Frank; she was completely dilated! When he came in, they had already moved her to the delivery room; at eleven thirteen we had a beautiful and healthy baby girl!

Dr. Robert was in the delivery room; he dried the little girl, and she cried spontaneously. It was so good to hear; we never heard Jorge Luis cry, so it was reassuring. After a few minutes Dr. Robert brought the baby to Angela and told us she appeared healthy. Then he turned to me and said softly, "Dr. Rojas." He used to call me that. "I think she is a little early." It took me a minute to figure out what he was saying, but she definitely looked a little premature. Later, when she was weighed, we found she was only five pounds and thirteen ounces. It seemed like somehow we were wrong in our dates; she was probably thirty-five or thirty-six weeks at the most! Till now I don't know where we went wrong.

We named her after her mother as it was the tradition in our families: Angela Maria, born Tuesday, November 8, 1977. Dr. William, our new pediatrician, gave us a clean bill of health; he was a recent Vanderbilt pediatrics graduate, and we would always be thankful for his calm demeanor. On the other hand, Dr. Mildred stormed into our room that afternoon, and the first words out of her mouth were "*George, that is no term baby; you should have not let them deliver her. I am glad she is breathing well!*" I knew exactly what she meant, but there was not much I could do about it. In her own way she was telling us she was happy for us, or at least that was what we thought.

Three days later we went home, and our lives would never be the same again. Even though we had a baby home before, this was a whole new ball of wax. Jorge Luis rarely cried. Gelita (that is what I always call her) cried a lot, and we would pick her up and carry her around all the time. I think she eventually learned to manipulate us well! We did not sleep much for the first six weeks. I went back to work after the first week; going to work was a relief.

Vanderbilt was self-insured, so our bill was covered by the insurance at 80 percent. The hospital bill had been a little over a $1,000 dollars; we only had to pay $200. My salary as a fellow was now about $30,000 a year, and we were able to pay it without a problem. As with Jorge Luis, we did not get any bills from the physicians.

It wasn't until we had our first pediatrician office visit that Dr. William told us it was all our fault. Gelita was healthy. We were just too nervous, and there was nothing wrong in letting her cry. He told us, "Feed her, put her in her crib, and walk away; you are not allowed to pick her up anymore. You may peek at her, but don't let her see you." We went home and tried it; it was hard to do, but after a few minutes she would stop crying and either go to sleep or entertain herself with the mobile in the crib.

As time went on Angela seemed more comfortable with her; she was enjoying being a mother of a normal child. I stayed a little distant. I would look at her and would see some of her features resemble Jorge Luis, and I would secretly worry. But as she grew older and more interactive, I started to enjoy her, too.

My training as a fellow in neonatology was progressing well. Vanderbilt was a very busy nursery, and we got to see many patients with all kinds of problems. I learned a lot from Dr. Mildred, through her rounds and discussions. She was always very approachable. Dr. Cotton and Dr. Dan introduced me to the use of computers in research and Dr. Hakan, to the intricacies of animal research. By the end of the academic year, I was very satisfied with my choice of program. Vanderbilt had been the right choice.

I also got a taste of academic medicine; in April I published my first abstract. We sent it to the Federation of American Societies for Experimental Biology, and it was chosen for presentation at their April meeting. The meeting was in Atlantic City, and both Dr. Hakan and Dr. Mildred came. I practiced my presentation a million times, but I was scared; this was the biggest audience I had ever addressed. Fortunately, all went well. The presentation went without a glitch, and the questions afterward were easy. Dr. Mildred told me before I went up to the podium, "Remember you know more about your project than anybody else; you can handle any question." Those words have stayed with me throughout my career.

My second year of fellowship was as successful as the first one; I continued to learn the tools of research. The use of computers in patient care fascinated me. I learned a lot from Dan; he started me on the basics of computer programing and data analysis. The department owned their own computer, which was located right at the nursery next to Dr. Bob's office. They had created a database of all the patients who had been admitted to the NICU for several years, so it was possible to evaluate changes over time as well as outcomes and do it by whatever group of babies or diagnosis you were interested in. This was one of the most valuable tools I was ever exposed to. It was a way of evaluating what you were doing.

Unfortunately, I was a little disappointed with the clinical side of the fellowship. Even though I learned a lot from Dr. Mildred's talks and rounds, the fellows were second-class citizens in the NICU. The residents ran the show, and they pretended to know it all and never wanted our input. Many times if I felt very strongly about something I would have to go to the attending physician because the residents would not listen to me. It was a little frustrating.

The fellows did all the transports. When we went out to pick up a baby our goal was always to bring the baby back in the best condition and treatment started if possible. The Angel One van was not just an ambulance but a mobile intensive care unit. We would treat the baby as if it was already admitted to the NICU. On arrival, we would check the baby out to the resident, and they would take over its care. It was frustrating when the baby was doing well and stable but the resident would decide to change the treatment we had already started. We had absolutely no voice once the baby was in the hands of the resident.

I also got to publish my first research article, along with Dr. Hakan and Dr. Robert, on the work we were doing on the lambs, in a journal called *Prostaglandins*. It was an eye-opening experience on how hard it was to publish. How reviewers saw your work was not always pleasant, and having to make changes was rather painful, but it taught me how to be flexible and listen to what the reviewer had to say.

Dr. Robert and I got very involved with Dr. Dan and Dr. Cotton in computer modeling. We knew that many newborn diseases were very predictable. We started collecting data of many babies and created models that we hoped could be used as a background to predict which babies were not doing as expected and an intervention was needed. This was fascinating work—I loved it!

During my second year, I also got involved with Dr. Kenneth, an adult pulmonologist who had developed a sheep model to study lung lymphatic fluid production. I spent a lot of time in his lab learning the technique, and eventually we reproduced the model in a lamb. The hours I spent in surgery with sheep and lambs would become very important in my career as a neonatologist.

The new model opened the door to many studies on lambs. At the end of my second year I had published eleven papers and had been invited to give several presentations. I gradually became very comfortable giving talks and handling questions, always remembering the words of Dr. Mildred: "You know more about your project than anybody else."

At home things were going well. Our daughter Gelita was now a year old and kept Angela very busy. We really enjoyed her; she had a happy, bubbly personality and made us laugh a lot. I also had a little more time off, so we were able to spend time together, and my salary as a fellow was a little better.

The owners of the nice town house we had been renting notified us that the complex was to become a condominium, and we only had two choices: either buy it or move out at the end of our contract. We were happy there, but the price was high, and we could not afford it. So we moved to a duplex in the south side of town. It had two bedrooms, a kitchen, a small dining area, and living room. It was not as nice as the townhouse, but it was reasonable.

Unfortunately, after we moved in we noticed a bad smell all over the house. It seemed as if the previous owner had had cats, and even though the carpet had been cleaned, the smell was in the padding. The owner, who lived on the other side of the duplex, agreed, and they replaced all the carpeting. It was nice to start with a clean carpet.

The landlady was very nice to us; she was sometimes even too friendly. She would go out of her way to check on Angela and would come to visit a lot. One day she invited us to her side, and we noticed that our names were in her project list on the refrigerator! We finally figured out that she was Mormon, and she was working on trying to recruit us. We made it clear we were Catholics, and that was the end of the friendship.

Late on in my second year, a new attending physician joined the faculty; Dr. Jay was a young, very bright, neonatologist. He was a good clinician and was interested in neonatal nutrition. He had actually worked on the development of the first formula specifically designed for premature babies. It was refreshing to see somebody with other interests besides the respiratory system.

Dr. Jay also had different ideas from the traditional Vanderbilt way and had many heated discussions during our weekly meetings. Dr. Mildred did not seem to like him initially but eventually learned to respect his different point of view. For us in training, it was a good thing to be exposed to a different point of view.

By June of my second year, I was still very uncertain of what my future was going to be. I had looked for positions in neonatology and had been offered a couple of positions back in Texas. I was uncertain whether I should go into clinical neonatology or stay in academia. I loved research, and I did not want to give it up.

I decided to consult with Dr. Mildred; she had always given me good advice. So I asked her secretary to get me an appointment with her in the next few days, and I warned her I needed at least an hour. The next morning she told me that Dr. Mildred also wanted to talk to me, so she wanted me in her office that same day at 5:00 p.m.

That evening, I went to her office, and Dr. Bob and Dr. Hakan were also there. I felt a little uneasy; she asked me what I wanted to talk to her about. I said I had questions about what I wanted to do in the future and wanted to run it by her. She told me she had the perfect advice; then she offered me a faculty position as an assistant professor. I was speechless. What a dream! I immediately accepted, and she got up and gave me a hug. Dr. Bob and Dr. Hakan followed, and I left the office walking on clouds. I could not wait to tell Angela.

I went straight to the phone, and I told her, "I am an assistant professor at Vanderbilt University!"

Chapter 11
ACADEMIC LIFE AND MEDICINE

By July 1, 1979, I had my own office. My first priority was to figure out how I could start doing some of my own research. I was full of ideas! Dr. Mildred recommended that I apply for a junior faculty grant through the university. I had never applied for a grant before; I did not even know where to start, but everybody in the division was willing to help, and I got it written and turned it in to the university administration.

In the meantime I continued to work on the data that we had collected on our previous experiments. Unfortunately, Dr. Robert was gone; he had finished his fellowship and gone back home. I sat down by myself with those long sheets of paper, adding up columns and calculating means and standard deviations. It was a very tedious and time-consuming job. Dr. Dan walked into my office one day and saw me doing it and said that I could be doing it on the computer much faster. I had worked with him a little on the database, but I had no idea how to do it; he said he would set up a terminal for me in my office, and I could use the university's mainframe.

Within a few days, I had a terminal on my desk, and Dr. Dan taught me how to sign in to the mainframe and use a spreadsheet program called Lotus. I will always be thankful to Dr. Dan for this; it was like walking into a new world. There were so many possibilities! Within a few days, I was using statistical programs to analyze my data and discovered a computer language called Basic, which was simple enough to learn and write my own programs. I was sold on computers!

The discovery of the computer early in my academic life was what people call an epiphany. I could see in my mind many practical uses for it, especially for the things that we did every day like calculating fluids and calories for the babies.

Within a few weeks, I had finished going through all my data on previous experiments and was able to write more abstracts for scientific meetings and got to present my work in a couple of research meetings. It was exciting to be part of the faculty; everybody in the division was very helpful and made me feel part of the team.

Then my big debut came; I was going to be the attending physician in the NICU for the first time in my life. I was determined to teach the residents the care of the babies down to every detail. I had a very good role model; I wanted my rounds to be as good as Dr. Mildred's rounds. The first few days, I think, the residents hated me because I was slow and took a long time to go through every patient because I asked for every detail and discussed every possibility. With time the residents got better at presenting their patients, and everything went smoothly.

The residents seemed to like my style; I enjoyed teaching more than any other thing I had been doing. The more information I gave the residents, the more they seemed to want. Slowly we started having a real discussion, and I could see that they read more and prepared themselves for rounds just as I did. It was fun! We discussed the babies' course and made a plan to follow on each baby's care. For me the most important thing was to make the residents think for themselves. I did not want to tell them what to do; I wanted them to figure out the best course of action. My goal was to develop thinking doctors, not just ones who follow protocols.

Vanderbilt had many things that bothered me, and I was determined to change them. One example was that every baby on a respirator got a chest X-ray every morning routinely. I started to make the residents think: Why do I need an X-ray? And not to order one unless there was a good reason. It was not long before I was called to Dr. Bob's office and told that a daily X-ray, whether the baby needed it or not, guaranteed that the residents would not miss something. I was disappointed that my argument of letting the residents think did not seem to be a valid one for Dr. Bob.

I had many frustrating mornings when I would make rounds and find out that the night resident had changed the plan we had agreed upon. The PL1 would just say that it was a PL3 on call, and he felt differently. I would get very angry and call the responsible resident. They just ignored me most of the time.

Another one of my pet peeves was the delivery room management of the babies. There is no more important time in the life of a baby than the first few moments of life. Initiating respirations and ensuring a normal heart rate are crucial for normal survival. So many times the PL1s would tell me that they had tried several times to put a tube down the baby's trachea unsuccessfully and that, finally, after the third attempt the PL2 finally got it in. This was unacceptable for me; I was determined to teach the residents how to do a good resuscitation and be proficient in intubation.

I asked the residents to call me before they went to the delivery room and allow me to teach them how to do it efficiently. I also spent hours teaching them how to intubate properly. In the delivery room, I allow the resident one attempt, and if it was unsuccessful, I would take over and do it, as I taught them the correct way. Thankfully, I have always been very proficient and never missed one. The PL1s and some of the PL2s were very thankful, but most of the PL3s were not happy.

The more I attended in the NICU, the more the residents seemed to like my rounds. They had gotten used to my style, and they would pride themselves when they had read something I hadn't. This was for me what rounds were supposed to be, an exchange of information with the baby's benefit in mind. Unfortunately, the older residents, who were used to being able to control everything, did not like my style.

A few months into my first year as a faculty member, I was called to the office of the chairman of pediatrics. Dr. David asked me why I was attending the delivery room with the residents. I told him that I wanted to make sure that they learned the proper resuscitation technique, and I felt that was the best way to do it. He proceeded to tell me that it was the second- and third-level residents' job to do that. I argued that many of them were not proficient, and I felt I could teach them, too. We had a heated discussion, but at the end I was told I was interfering with the residents' hierarchy, and I was banned from doing it anymore.

I could not understand the reasoning behind the whole thing. I went back to my office very frustrated and angry. Faculty members were supposed to teach; what was I supposed to do? I knew which residents were responsible for the complaint, so I tried to stay away from them, but I continued to teach those who wanted to learn.

I also started to work on simple programs to help the house staff. It was easy to write programs that would take the baby's weight and calculate the baby's fluids and calories or calculate exactly how much blood to give a baby to raise its blood count to a desired level. The residents loved my little programs. Once we had a baby that was born very anemic with a blood count of 16; the question was how big an exchange transfusion needed to be done. Using one of my programs, we calculated the amount of blood to be exchanged, and did it based on those numbers. We started at 16 and ended at 45 just as calculated.

The next morning at Dr. Mildred's rounds, when the resident presented the baby's history and what had been done, she said that was impossible to calculate. The resident pulled out the calculations done by my program, step by step, and Dr. Mildred just looked at me and said her usual "Good job!" and laughed as she walked away. I could not hide my satisfaction; I grinned for hours.

At the end of my first year as attending, the house staff gave me an award. I was completely unaware of it. On the last Grand Rounds of the year, as I walked into the auditorium, I saw Angela in the audience. I asked her, "What are you doing here?"

She just smiled and said, "You'll see."

As Grand Rounds started, the chairman Dr. David announced that they would give the awards voted by the house staff. The Amos Christie Award named after the previous chairman of pediatrics was given to two people, a private pediatrician and a faculty member. They called Dr. William, our pediatrician, and he went up to the podium and accepted the award. Then, they called my name! I was certainly not expecting it; I was speechless. I went up to the chairman and he gave me the award, and I just stood there with everybody applauding. I did not know what to say, so I just said, "Thank you" and got off the stage. It was something I will never forget; the award still hangs at home among my most precious things. It reads:

AMOS CHRISTIE AWARD
CHILDREN'S HOSPITAL
OF VANDERBILT UNIVERSITY

PRESENTED TO THE FACULTY
MEMBER WHOSE TEACHING,
BY WORD AND EXAMPLE, HAS
BEEN MOST OUTSTANDING

JORGE ROJAS, MD

1981
FROM THE HOUSE STAFF
WITH THANKS AND APPRECIATION

I am sure I was glowing when I left the auditorium, truly one of the dearest awards I have ever received in my lifetime. Maybe a tribute to my obstinacy; I could not help grinning when Dr. David shook my hand that day.

In those days, there was a belief that a large amount of fluid was essential to stop labor, so it was not unusual for mothers to get several liters of fluid in an attempt to stop labor. If labor did not stop, and the baby was delivered, it was common to see babies that were born puffy with low serum sodium. These babies tended to be the sickest, with their lungs stiff and requiring high pressure on the ventilator. These babies also had a high incidence of ruptured lungs.

I was bothered by this finding and asked one of the new fellows, Dr. Petaiah, to look at a group of these babies, and I recruited Kathy, an obstetrical nurse, to collect data on the fluids given to the mothers. Soon we found out that the mothers who got the largest amount of fluids had the babies with the lowest serum sodium. This finding prompted another research project: we had to prove that the babies were fluid overloaded.

After much research and discussion with other members of the faculty, we decided to try to actually measure the amount of water in the babies. We found a method to measure extracellular water volume in premature babies by administering a small dose of bromide right after delivery, allowing the bromide to distribute throughout the body and then obtaining samples of blood. We could then calculate the total amount of water in the baby.

It was a very intense project. We had to be there at the hospital imme-diately after the baby's birth, obtain permission from the parents to enter the baby in the study, get a sample of blood, and administer the bromide as soon as the baby had an intravenous line. Then we had to wait three hours and obtain a second sample. The samples had to be spun immediately and the plasma separated and frozen. Also, we had to collect all the informa-tion on the amount of fluids the mother received and keep track of the baby's urine output and fluid intake during the first five days of life. Dr. Petaiah and Kathy were amazing troopers, and we eventually collected thirty consecutive babies, but we spent many nights in the hospital. I was not taking call anymore, but it seemed like research kept me away from home just as much.

What followed was the analysis of the samples and all the calcula-tions to finally determine the amount of extracellular water in the babies. Fortunately, my computer skills were much better, and we were able to get all the data analyzed in a couple of months. We were right! The babies with the lower sodium had the higher water volumes and the mothers the larger amounts of fluids. We went out and celebrated!

Then the hardest phase began; we had to write it up and send it to a journal. I had written some papers before with other people, but for the first time I was the principal investigator. I decided to split things: I gave Dr. Petaiah the job of looking up all the references we needed for the neo-natal side and the bromide space method and gave to Kathy the obstetrical side. My job was to start an outline of the paper.

Within a week, we had done our assignments, and I gave both what I had written and asked them for their opinion. Dr. Petaiah and I had the disadvantage that English was not our first language, but Kathy on the other hand was excellent in English. About four or five revisions later, we had what we thought was a finished product, and I took it to Dr. Mildred and asked her for her opinion. Needless to say she read it and had thousands of suggestions. Eventually, she thought it was journal ready, and we sent it to the *Journal of Pediatrics*.

Several weeks later, we got a letter with opinions from three reviewers; they would consider the paper for publication if we agreed to make some minor modifications. Wow! I was beyond happy; this was my first paper as principal investigator! Everybody in the department congratulated us; I felt like I was beginning to be part of the faculty for real.

I also participated in many projects in the sheep lab, which resulted in several publications. During my stay at Vanderbilt, I published a total of eighteen papers. I was doing well as an academician, but as a clinician I was not satisfied.

I was still having troubles adjusting to the academic way of teaching the residents and how we were taking care of the patients. As a clinician I knew every baby was different, and I wanted to teach the residents to recognize these differences, look at the babies carefully, do good physical exams, and take good histories. This was what I was trained to do during my residency, and this was what Dr. Mildred preached on her rounds, but this was not what the academic environment promoted. There were tight protocols, daily lab work, and daily X-rays; the residents were not taught to think and that continued to bother me.

Consulting specialists was very common, but in many instances it was because the residents did not want to spend the time thinking and investigating but rather call somebody else to tell them what was wrong with their baby. A murmur meant a cardiologist, poor urine output, a nephrologist, anemia, a hematologist. I would get frustrated every day trying to make the residents think for themselves and getting no response. One of my best teachers, Dr. Alexander, used to teach us that calling a specialist was only to confirm our diagnosis, not to think for us. I did not seem to be able to get this message across to the residents.

Things at home were well; in June of 1980, at the end of my first year as a member of the faculty, Angela gave birth to our second child. Another beautiful girl! We named her Laura Elena, not particularly after anybody; we just liked the names. As usual Angela had a very fast labor. We had a new obstetrician, Dr. John; he seemed to be more understanding and patient than Dr. Frank.

It was induced labor again, but this time at a certain thirty-nine weeks gestation. Within forty-five minutes of the start of the induction, Angela was ready to push and delivered in just over an hour. When I told the nurse she was ready to push, she would not believe it. I insisted that she check her. Been there before! As soon as she did, she called the doctor and said, "Dr. John, she is complete and pushing; you better hurry." Dr. John got there barely on time, but all went well, and we went home three days later with our second baby girl.

Having two children at home kept Angela very busy, and, unfortunately, I was so involved with work and research that I was not home a lot. I was working long hours either in the sheep lab or in the nursery, or was analyzing data. With two children, expenses at home were increasing, and my first-year faculty paycheck was just not enough. The transition from fellow to faculty did not give me a big increase in pay, but it gave me a big increase in responsibilities. I was spending more time at work than at home. I was beginning to question if this was what I really wanted to do.

During my first year as faculty, Angela and I also made the decision to buy a house. We had researched the available loans, and we found a graduated loan that had very small payments in the first two years and then increased yearly. The first few years were no different from our duplex rent, so we decided to give it a try.

We had found a brand new house not far from where we were living; it had a large living room, a nice kitchen, three bedrooms, two baths, and a full basement with a garage. The down payment was small, and we closed the deal in a few days. We were now homeowners but had the responsibilities of not only the mortgage but also the maintenance of the house. So I decided I would try again to see if I could get an increase in my salary.

I went to talk with Dr. Mildred; she had always given me good advice. We discussed the salary first, and she was very certain that the chairman of the department would not approve an increase, but there was an opportunity to allow me to moonlight. She knew that the neonatologist at the special care nursery (SCN) at the local Baptist Hospital was looking for some nights off, and I could do that. She also suggested that I might consider delegating parts of my research responsibilities to the fellows; that would give me more time to be home.

I tackled the first suggestion first. I went to see the neonatologist at Baptist Hospital. His name was Dr. Tom; he was very nice, showed me around the SCN, and we talked about moonlighting. He was the only neonatologist, so he had to be available twenty-four hours. He suggested we start by me covering for him from 5:00 p.m. to 5:00 a.m. once a week, and if it worked out we could increase it. He explained to me that the unit was only an intermediate care unit, so anything that would require any kind of respiratory support would have to be transferred to Vanderbilt.

The logistics were quite different from Vanderbilt though; all patients belonged to a private pediatrician, so most of the time we had to wait until we were consulted to participate in the care of the baby. This seemed OK. I had no idea how it was going to work out, but I decided to give it a try, especially after he told me the hospital would be paying me $1,000 for every twelve-hour shift I worked. Wow! This was unbelievable; it was like making every week what I used to make in a month!

I got home and told Angela, and at first she was excited. But on second thoughts she knew this would mean more time away from home. We figured I could do it until hopefully Vanderbilt would increase my salary and then I could stop, but now the money would be very welcome.

My first night at Baptist was a memorable one; I went in and checked in with Dr. Tom. We walked through the SCN, and he showed me the six babies that were admitted. All but one were growing healthy premature babies with no major problems and the sixth one a term baby getting antibiotics because his mother had an infection during labor; he also appeared healthy.

I also met the nurses; they were all very nice. The charge nurse in the evening was Carol; she was very supportive and just told me if I had any questions to just ask her. She was different, sweet, but ran her shift like a sergeant; things got done or else!

After that I went home and told them how to get in touch with me at home and carried Dr. Tom's beeper. It was a very simple paging device; when the nurses needed me they would send me a number to call. In those days, this was state of the art. I went home, and all was well until midnight, when I got a call from the head nurse, whose name was Jennifer, and she told me Dr. Paul had a premature baby, about thirty-five weeks gestation that needed oxygen and that he requested my help. He could not talk to me because he was trying to put an umbilical artery line.

I jumped out of bed, put my scrubs on, and headed for the hospital. When I arrived, Dr. Paul, an older pediatrician, told me the baby was on 50 percent oxygen, and he had attempted to put a line but failed. I told him I would take care of the baby, and he left to talk to the mother. I examined the baby; he was very pink and not in much distress, Dr. Paul had cut the umbilical cord very short and none of the arteries were visible. I drew an arterial blood gas sample out of his wrist and sent it to the lab. When the results came back his oxygen was extremely high. I told the nurses to wean the oxygen down slowly as long as the baby remained pink.

Within an hour the baby was on room air. I rechecked blood gas, and it was normal. Even though the baby was breathing a little fast, he was otherwise well and appeared hungry. I asked the nurses to offer him a little sugar water. They looked at me surprised but did it, and the baby took it fine. Being a little premature, the baby likely had some trouble establishing respirations but was now fine. I gave them instructions on how to continue small feedings, wrote the history, physical exam, and orders in the chart and went to talk to the mother.

As I explained to the mother that I thought the baby was fine, just needed to take things easy since he was a little early, I became an instant hero! She was very thankful; I took the father back to the nursery and went home with just enough time to clean up and go to work. Even though I was tired, this new experience gave me back a little of what I was craving for at Vanderbilt, just being in control of my patient and communicating with parents. I felt really good about my first experience moonlighting.

Later that morning, Dr. Tom called me at work and told me I had forgotten to put any charges. This was new to me; I told him I was not sure what he was talking about, so he explained to me that after every patient encounter I was supposed to fill in a charge sheet; he had forgotten to show me that. But he would do it for me and show me next time where everything was.

He explained to me that there were three charges I could pick from for my initial contact with the baby; they were based on how much time I had spent and what I had to do with the baby; basically they were called brief, intermediate, and comprehensive and roughly corresponded to twenty, forty, and sixty minutes. He told me that for an admission like that it never took less than an hour, so he always used the comprehensive level. I thought that was appropriate for this baby also. Then he asked me if I did any procedures; I told me I drew arterial gases twice; he told me we had to charge for those, too.

This was very educational, for since my initial work as a graduate student several years before, I had never had to deal with charging for my services; as an intern, resident, or fellow we got paid a salary and never knew what the university charged for our work. This was my first experience with how to charge for what I was doing. I had no idea of how much money was charged for all these things. But I was eager to learn more about it.

A couple of days later, I called Dr. Tom and asked him if I could come over and discuss the charging stuff. He met with me that same afternoon and went over how things were done. He showed me the charge sheet that every baby had; it contained the baby's name, date of birth, and then a series of codes with their description. There were charges for initial day, subsequent days, consultations, and about fifteen common procedures. He would just write the date that things were done. On the back was a long list of common diagnosis, which you had to pick; all of them had a code, too.

These sheets would be sent to the business office after the babies' discharge, and they would bill the insurance company and the parents. It all seemed very simple. The charges for my first patient were $300 for the initial day and $40 for each of the arterial punctures I did. He explained to me that some insurance paid more than others, and the parents were responsible for the rest. It all appeared simple and made sense to me.

During the next few months, I covered many nights for Dr. Tom, and I enjoyed every minute of it. It was so much fun to come in and have complete control of the patient and spend time talking with the parents. Also, I got to meet several of the local pediatricians, who slowly started to trust me more and more. Eventually, many of them would ask the nurses to call me even before they had seen the baby. Most of them actually wanted to learn what I was doing and seemed thankful that they did not have to deal with it.

I also decided to always call the pediatrician after I had stabilized the baby and always keep them in the loop. They seemed to like this, and it was good for me since many of them already knew the families, and I was a new face in their lives and could use all the help I could get to gain their confidence.

My work at Vanderbilt continued as always, more sheep experiments, more data to analyze, and when I was in the clinical service more frustrations with the residents. Things were better economically; the checks from Baptist Hospital for $1,000 per night went a long way to help things at home. Unfortunately, I was actually spending less time at home because of the added night calls. Angela as usual was a good trooper and took care of me, the house, and the kids without ever complaining.

It was now my second year as a faculty member; I had become well versed in using computers, and with the guidance of Dr. Dan, we worked on developing a computer model of the course of hyaline membrane disease, for babies born with immature lungs. They always seem follow a very predictable pattern: they get worse the first twenty hours, then stabilize, and at about seventy-two hours, start to get better. We collected information in over thirty-one uncomplicated babies and constructed a statistical model using a function that combined the values of how much oxygen and how much pressure the babies needed to remain stable throughout the first ninety-six hours of life. We actually divided the babies by severity and came up with a very tight model that allowed us to predict within the first six hours of life a new baby's course over the next ninety hours. This allowed us to raise a red flag when a baby was not following a predicted course and diagnose complications early.

This statistical modeling work taught me a lot about the use of computers in medicine and eventually produced three publications: two journals articles and one chapter in a book. As an academician, I was doing very well. In my five years as a fellow and now a faculty member, I had done work that resulted in several publications. I loved research, and I had learned a lot, but I was still frustrated on the clinical side. Every time I was attending, I would get frustrated at the politics within the house staff. The junior residents seemed to like me, but the senior ones seemed to resent me.

I got along well with all the members of the neonatology division. I enjoyed specially our weekly research meetings, where we presented what we were working on or new ideas we wanted to develop. There would be a discussion among the group, and usually Dr. Mildred would destroy our theories in a few seconds. She was tough, but I learned how to have an honest approach to research from her. We very rarely discussed clinical problems; only Dr. Jay would bring up issues from the NICU, but it seemed like he was always either ignored or criticized.

Dr. Jay was nice and supportive of me, I guess because we were the two youngest members of the faculty. He was very different from the other faculty members, who always focused on the respiratory system; his interest was in neonatal nutrition, and he had done some research for one of the formula companies. He believed that formula was the best thing for the babies, and he would push the new formulas he had helped develop.

Unfortunately, I have always been a believer in breast milk, and all the babies born during my attending rotation were started on breast milk with added calories. Dr. Jay followed me and even though they were doing well, within a few days all these babies would be taken off breast milk and placed on fortified formula. I would get very angry, and the house staff would tell me there was nothing they could do.

I talked to Dr. Mildred about it, but it was obvious she was not going to get involved; it was the prerogative of the attending physician to determine the best treatment for his patients during his rotation. It was very frustrating, and I had no way to change it.

Eventually, many years later, research showed that the mother's milk was the best food for premature babies. Currently, many breast milk banks exist for cases where the mother cannot provide it. It is one of those things that make me want to say, "I told you so!" every time I see it.

In February, things got more complicated. Angela found out that we were expecting our third child. I felt that I needed to be home more, and with the added calls at Baptist and my research projects, I just was not being much help to Angela. Something had to change.

I went to see Dr. Mildred again and explained my situation. She told me that such was the life of the true academician and that there was no way I could slow down my work and remain in the faculty. I explained about what I felt was my obligation to my family, and her answer was "George, you just have to give up on some of those things."

I left her office very disturbed; I could not make her understand that my family was the most important thing to me. I guess she never had a family, and it was hard for her to understand it. As much as I respected her as a professor and as much as she had taught me as a clinician, this was something she did not seem to understand.

I continued to work nights at Baptist covering for Dr. Tom, and I was beginning to really like it. I was doing what I really loved, which was taking care of babies. I was meeting new pediatricians and talking to families, all the things that were not my job as a faculty member at Vanderbilt. The nurses at the SCN were fantastic down-to-earth people who seemed honestly open to learn anything I could teach them. I was having fun, but I was getting no rest with both jobs.

Angela's pregnancy was progressing well; her due date was going to be very close to the birthdate of our firstborn, Jorge Luis. That was a scary thought, but there was not much we could do. She had her hands full with the girls now two and four years old; I guess she did not have much time to even think about it.

Then, the phone call came that would change my life forever.

Dr. Arville, the chief of pediatrics at Baptist, called me at home. He explained to me that Dr. Tom really needed permanent help at Baptist, and the hospital had thought of hiring a second full-time neonatologist. Since I was already working for Dr. Tom, and I knew the system, they wanted to offer me the job first. He also told me that many of the pediatricians were behind the request. The administration wanted to meet with me if I would consider the offer. I was astonished; this was something I was not expecting. I told him to give me a few days to think about it.

I went home and discussed it with Angela. She was all for it if it would mean that I would be home more, but she pointed out that her pregnancy would not be covered if I left Vanderbilt before the birth. This was something to consider carefully. So we decided that I would meet with the administration at Baptist and find out more details.

I few days later, I met with Mr. David and Mr. Paul, the president and vice-president of the hospital. They were very nice and explained to me that it was not only help for Dr. Tom that they were looking for; they also wanted someone who would help grow the unit to the next level so that babies would not have to be sent to Vanderbilt. They offered me $75,000 a year, and I would get health insurance through the hospital group. They also pledged to support me on whatever I would need to develop the unit.

Wow! This was a lot of food for thought.

Chapter 12

THE BAPTIST YEARS AND GROWING AN NICU

It was not long before Angela and I decided that going to Baptist was the best decision to make. We knew that I would be on call every other day and every other weekend, but the money was very good, and we needed it. Also, the service was not very busy, and even though my job was to develop the NICU, hopefully, as we grew, we would be able to hire more neonatologists. We knew it was a gamble, but we were willing to take the risk!

I waited until the end of August to go talk to Dr. Mildred. Our third child was due in the first week of September, and I could not leave before he was born because we would lose our insurance coverage. It would be six weeks' notice, so I felt it was appropriate. Yes! I said "he"; we knew by ultrasound that this one was a boy!

When I talked to Dr. Mildred, she seemed very disappointed; she told me she saw a bright academic future for me, but she understood my reasons. I think for the first time she actually understood how important my family was to me. I felt bad, but I also knew I could not be the academician she wanted me to be. I loved direct patient care, and it would never happen at Vanderbilt.

I admire her for all that she stood for, and I felt bad to disappoint her, but I know now that was one of the best decisions I made in my lifetime. As I left I became teary eyed and she did, too.

Telling my decision to all the nurses, residents, and interns was also very hard. The rest of the faculty did not seem to care one way or another, but all wished me well. My last day at Vanderbilt would be September 30, 1982.

Angela was doing well, slowly approaching term and being reassured by Dr. John. He did not want to induce her and was hoping she will go into labor by herself. I was a little scared; I knew how fast her labors were and I was afraid that if I wasn't home she may deliver without me!

We had planned to have the girls with us in the delivery room; we had all gone to classes, and Kim, one of the nurses who worked in the transport van, was going to be their coach. She had prepared bags for them to keep busy, and we were all set for the big day.

Then it happened! On September 3, we went to bed, and within a few minutes Angela woke me up and said, "My water just broke!" I went into panic mode, picked up the bags, and as Angela got ready I called Kim and got the girls ready, and we were all in the car and on our way to the hospital in no time.

I was trying to stay calm and not speed, but Angela seemed very quiet and I even heard a grunt or two. As soon as we arrived at the hospital, we went through admissions quickly, and they took us up to our LDR (labor-delivery-recovery) room. Kim was already there and took care of the girls while Angela put on the hospital gown and lay down on the bed. The nurse and Dr. John came in, and he went on to check her progress.

The nurse was trying to get a heart rate through Angela's belly and yelled in a panic, "Dr. John, I cannot hear the baby's heart rate."

Dr. John responded, "That is because the baby is down here! He is crowning."

It did not take Angela but four good pushes, and little Jorge was born. It took exactly forty-seven minutes from the time she broke her water to the time she delivered. We almost did not make it to the hospital on time!

I was a very proud man, not only of how well Angela had done, but also of the fact that I was finally the father of a baby boy!

A few days later we went home, Angela to her super-busy routine with three little ones at home and me back to Vanderbilt, where I was trying desperately to finish all the projects I had pending while continuing to cover nights for Dr. Tom at Baptist, getting to know the staff, and thinking of how things could be improved there to slowly become a level-three nursery.

I had made a lot of good friends, and I felt somewhat bad at leaving, but I thought that was best for me and my family. The last few days were the hardest; some people felt I had betrayed them by going across the street to what they felt was the competition.

October 1, 1982, a Friday, was my official first day at Baptist. Dr. Tom was happy that I was there to help. We spent all day going over what needed to be done every day and talked about making a schedule that would give us every other weekend off. We would be on call one week: Monday, Wednesday, and Friday through Sunday and the next week only Tuesday and Thursday. This seemed better than a straight every other day.

Every morning, we had several normal babies that did not have an in-town pediatrician to be examined or discharged and then talked to their mothers. Then we made rounds on the babies in the NICU, and the one on call would be available for any consultations or new admissions. It took us a good part of the morning to do these chores and write down all our charges. Then we went for lunch at the doctor's dining room, which was free, and stayed in the office till the afternoon and then went home.

I spent all my free time getting to know the nurses and finding out how they worked and how much they knew about things like using respirators and taking care of small babies. It was obvious that we had a long road ahead before we would be able to do any of that. I used to smoke then, as well as many of the nurses, so I would go to the break room and sit with the nurses in a smoke-filled room and chat. That was the best way to get to know them.

The NICU was in three small separate rooms, which was not very efficient, so my first project was to talk to the administration about knocking down the walls between the rooms and adding more oxygen and air outlets as well as electrical outlets. They were very receptive. An architect met with me and Dr. Tom, and we planned on how to do it in stages. The hospital was a very clean and simple structure; all the walls had light blue tiles and floors were terrazzo. Knocking walls out was an easy process, and in a few weeks we had doubled our space.

All the nurses seemed happy about it; communication was easier since all the patients were now in the same room, and they had designed their own pharmacy and supply areas so that it would be efficient. The only person who was not happy was Martha the clerk. She had her own little office, and now we had taken over that space and moved her out to a small corridor outside the patient area and she hated it. For a long time she did not like me, but eventually we became very good friends.

The staff was very receptive to all these changes and eager to learn more. We had a wonderful head nurse, June, who was older and very organized and knowledgeable and a small staff of nurses who were eager to learn. Each shift had a charge nurse, and they were all game for all I wanted to do. Scotland was charge nurse of the day shift, Carol of the evening shift and Jennifer of the night shift. Nurses then worked eight-hour shifts, so they were there five days a week; I got to know all of them very quickly.

First we started keeping babies that needed oxygen only and then a few that needed nasal continuous positive pressure (CPAP), and as we went we discovered things that needed to be changed and updated. Dr. Tom had a wonderful gift for writing very detailed policies and procedures, so we had to do very few changes to what he had already done. Teaching the nurses how to use intravenous catheters and how to take care of smaller babies was easy because they wanted to keep their babies and not have to send them to Vanderbilt.

I spent a lot of time with the nurses just talking about the care of the smaller and sicker babies. We went over feedings, IV fluids, skin care, and respirator management. They were so eager to learn! They all helped each other and passed on things to those on the other shifts.; It was like a big family, and everybody helped everybody. Not having to send babies to Vanderbilt was my ultimate goal, too.

We had no RTs, so the nurses did all the work related to the respirator. They took it apart after it had been used and packed it and took it to get it sterilized and when it came back put it back together. So they actually had a more intimate understanding of how the respirator worked than the nurses at Vanderbilt.

Each shift had its own personalities, and I spent as much time with them as I could. In the break room I learned a lot about their expectations. I slowly learned what their strengths and weaknesses were; I don't remember all their names, but some I will never forget. During the day, June and Scotland kept things moving and made sure the pediatricians were informed about their babies when they visited in the mornings.

Our charge nurse on evenings, Carol, was like a drill sergeant. Every evening she worked she would start by making sure the floor was clean and all the trash emptied. She would pick up a mop and do it herself if she needed to and made sure housekeeping did their job. Her shift always ran smoothly. Her second-in-command, Connie, a cute blonde also known as Barbie, kept things in shape when Carol was not there.

Night was an interesting shift. Most of the nurses were true night people; they worked the shift because they liked it. The charge nurse was Jennifer, an extremely intelligent nurse. She could have been a doctor if she wanted to. I always felt I could trust her with any decision and she would always do the right thing. Most of the other night nurses seemed to be older and more mature.

I had to learn everything about how the business of medicine works. Dr. Tom had his charge sheets and diagnosis codes, but we had to update all of them We were now doing things he had not done before, and we had a responsibility to make sure the charges were accurate so that the hospital could collect as much of our salaries as possible.

I sat down and studied the *Physicians' Current Procedural Terminology* book and learned as much about this side of medicine as I could. I made sure that our charge sheet was updated and that we included all the procedures and diagnosis we used. I just wanted to make sure that we got paid for what we did.

Then I followed those charge sheets downstairs to the hospital's business office and met the lady who did our charges. She taught me how she filled the insurance claim forms and sent them to the insurance companies for payment. It all seemed very straightforward. The checks would come in the mail to us; we would just sign them to the hospital, and the money went to help pay our salaries.

Most insurance companies paid us most of the charges after the patient deductible had been met or a percent their policy allowed. Then she would bill the rest directly to the family. At any time we were allowed to drop or forgive a bill if we wanted to, and we had the final say on whether they needed to be turned out to a collection agency, which I hated to do. I became very picky about whether they actually were able to pay.

Very quickly, I got an education on the side of medicine that nobody ever taught me before, neither in medical school nor during my training. But everything seemed to be straightforward. You billed a reasonable amount, and you got paid for what you did.

The administration was also responsive; anything I asked for I got. They used to tell me, "Whatever your little patients need we can provide." In a few weeks, we had everybody working for a common goal: not to send babies away anymore. The only thing they ever asked of me was that they wanted us to keep our charges low since they liked Baptist to be known as the most economical place in town to have a baby. They hoped that the large number of deliveries would compensate for it.

The only point of contention I had with the administration was the name of the NICU. For years it had been called the SCN, and I really wanted the name to be changed to NICU. Their argument was that NICU scared people, while SCN was soothing to the parents. Dr. Tom seemed to be OK with that so I gave up.

We started keeping smaller and sicker babies, until one day we had a baby that was twenty-three weeks gestation and just 600 g (one pound and five ounces) and needed a respirator. As I brought the baby to the unit, I placed him on the respirator, started his umbilical arterial line, and turned to the nurses and asked, "What do you want to do? Do you want to keep him?"

There were a few minutes of silence and then Scotland looked at me and said, "We want to keep him."

Up to that day, we had been able to go home early and just come back if needed. After that day, I knew that as long as a baby was on a respirator we would have to stay in the hospital. I will never forget this baby. His name was Javon, and it was October 2, 1983. That day we became a level-three nursery!

Javon was not an easy baby to take care of. He probably had every need that a baby that size could have. It was a learning experience for all of us. Sometimes we had the resources, but other times we improvised and learned. He was 119 days in the hospital, and I got to know his mother well. When he went home, we kept in touch, and thirty-five years later we still share a bond.

It was ironic that I had just had my one-year anniversary at Baptist Hospital the day we became a level-three nursery, but this was just the beginning. As we kept more small and sick babies, the obstetricians also felt more comfortable delivering those kinds of babies at Baptist, so the hospital's delivery numbers also increased. In the year 1983, Baptist had 4,416 deliveries and the SCN 290 admissions.

Dr. Tom had been very good about keeping track of the number of deliveries and admissions to the SCN, but I knew that if we really wanted to keep track of our patients we needed to keep a database with detailed information for every baby. The hospital did not have any computers that we could use, so I bought a Radio Shack Model Three computer and started my own database. I had learned from Dr. Dan at Vanderbilt how to do it, and what he had taught me was invaluable.

The first personal computer at Baptist Hospital was such an event that one day the director of nursing and the hospital's president came to my office along with a cameraman and took pictures. I was ecstatic!

We kept this database going for the next thirty-five years. I would generate a report every year for the administration, which they really appreciated. At one point when the Joint Commission on Accreditation of Hospitals (JCAH) came to inspect our unit, they were highly impressed that our data was readily available. We were again, a little ahead of our time.

We started with nine beds of which we considered only four to be intensive care; with time it became obvious that we would need more space. The administration was very supportive and tried to accommodate our growing needs. We added another room, which gave us another three beds for a total of twelve. We continued to keep most of our babies, only occasionally sending babies to Vanderbilt when they needed surgery, or when we did not have a respirator available.

The hospital owned only one baby respirator, but we needed more; we could rent them, but it became obvious that it would be better if we just bought them. The administration agreed and purchased two more respirators, but it became clear that the nurses did not have the time anymore to take care of them. We needed respiratory therapy support; so I went to the administration and requested it. They agreed to hire one therapist to cover during the day and take care of the machines. They seemed so pleased that the SCN was growing and we were not sending babies away anymore that I felt I could ask for anything.

I was practicing the kind of medicine I had always dreamed of; I was helping babies and working with the parents and their pediatricians to try to make things as smooth as possible during difficult times. I had developed a good relationship with most of the obstetricians, and most of all our nurses were learning and becoming the best staff in town. We were all very proud of what we had accomplished, and the administration was supportive of all we needed.

Economically, I had a good salary and had learned all the intricacies of billing and collecting. The patient population we were dealing with was insured about 90 percent of the time. The rest were usually Medicaid or no insurance. Insurance companies paid most of the bills. We took whatever payments the government assigned us and never turned anybody out for collection.

Even though we kept our charges low, by the end of the second year we had met our salaries, and I realized we were actually making money for the hospital. It was time to renegotiate our contract.

Tom and I went down to the administration and negotiated a new agreement. We would continue to cover the unit twenty-four hours and continue to develop the unit; our salary minimum would remain the same, but any money collected over the salary would belong to us. The billing clerk would be 100 percent under our control, and she would do our billing and any secretarial work we may need. She would bill the insurance companies for us, and the checks would come to us directly. We would handle the money and pay our salaries from it, and we would report our income to the hospital every six months. If the amount was less than our guarantee, the hospital would pay us the difference, and if it was higher we would add it to the next six months.

It all seemed reasonable; we would have control over our revenue, and the hospital would only pitch in if needed. I feel very proud that since that day, the hospital never had to pay us a penny. Unfortunately, I had to learn a whole new set of skills! Tom trusted me to handle the money, so I had to go to the bank and set up an account, and every month pay Tom and me our salary.

Nobody taught me any of this in medical school; I knew nothing about the business side of medicine. But I thought as long as we did our job and billed the appropriate amounts we should be fine.

Out of the blue I was in charge of a bank account, keeping track of payments, writing checks, and a whole new set of responsibilities. I had to learn about retirement plans, taxes, and even consult a lawyer to decide whether we needed to incorporate. Fortunately, people were always willing to help, and we decided to become a partnership, which would make things easier. The partnership Neonatology Professional Service was born.

Interestingly, the name happened due to a mistake on my part. I noticed that the hospital would always write Neonatology Professional Service in their records. I thought this was the name that Tom had been using, but it turned out that the billing clerk, not knowing what else to call it, came up with the name. We functioned under this name for the next twenty-three years till we sold the practice.

Over the next year, we continued to grow. Tom and I were spending pretty much all our time on call at the hospital: every other day and every other weekend. I felt bad that I did not spend a lot of time at home; our children were now seven, four, and two years old, and Angela had her plate full. The oldest was now going to school, and that brought her a new set of responsibilities from taking her to school, picking her up, making lunch, and helping with homework.

Angela would bring the kids to visit on Sundays when I worked the weekend, so we got to spend some time together when I was working, but most days I was tired by the time I got home. We were admitting more babies to the unit; we now had three respirators and a full staff of RTs. Our nursing staff also continued to grow. We had lots of new young nurses, so I spent a lot of my time teaching my approach to intensive care to the new nurses and continued to learn about the intricacies of nursing from the old ones.

We had never heard of the idea of *team* approach, but we had become a team. Nurses provided their inputs as they spent the most time with the babies, and we tailored each baby's care to its specific needs. We involved the pediatricians and the parents, and by the time the baby was ready to go home everything worked out. Some patients were easier than others, but this approach seemed to work well.

One of the obstetricians suggested that we should train our nurses and RTs to do newborn resuscitation and that would give more efficiency in handling delivery room calls, which were becoming very common. I researched it and could not find anything already available; so I decided to create my own program and called it the 2-4-1 program; it was a catchy way to teach people that there were *two* people, the nurse and the RT, *for* one baby.

I designed a set of conferences that covered the physiology of birth and what can go wrong and also a set of skills that they would master and be checked on to become part of the 2-4-1 Team. I even designed buttons that I was planning to give to those who finished the course. Unfortunately, the then director of nursing, Ms. Evelynn, banned the buttons! Her argument was that buttons were used by unions and that was not allowed. I had already ordered fifty of them, which will remain in a drawer forever. But the program was a success; all the staff in the SCN went through it and received their 2-4-1 certification. I felt comfortable that they could handle an emergency when we were not around. In a selfish way the program also benefited Tom and me.

The program drew the attention of the labor and delivery staff also. They were present at every delivery and in many instances had to take care of the baby while the SCN staff got there; so we got them involved in the training, and eventually everybody in our area was certified. The success of the program was much more than I ever anticipated, it sure made me proud. It became a requirement for all new staff; it reassured us that we would always have somebody trained in resuscitation present in the delivery room.

Several years later in 1987, the American Academy of Pediatrics started their NRP (Neonatal Resuscitation Program), which is now used around the world. Their program eventually replaced our 2-4-1 program at the hospital. I always felt that we were a little ahead of our time!

The year 1984 proved to be an even better year; the number of deliveries increased to 4,605, and we admitted 301 to the SCN. It meant that a little less than 7 percent of the babies required intensive care. This was a good number and comparable to other community hospitals. I was very pleased; over the next thirty years this number remained constant.

I also got more involved with the normal nursery and the nurses who worked in it. There were some very experienced people, and I always tried to listen to them when they were worried about a baby.

At Baptist all babies came to normal nursery first, unless we were involved in the delivery and took them directly to the SCN. There was an area which was next to the viewing windows where all the new babies were shown to the families. This was also an area where babies were watched for any problems immediately after their delivery. If they did well they were moved to other rooms where they were kept till it was time for them to go see their mothers.

This was very similar to the transitional care nursery I had been exposed to at the Robert B. Green Hospital in San Antonio; babies would be watched during their transitional period and even given oxygen if required, and they were transferred out when they were stable. Some of the nurses in this area had been doing this for years and had an enormous amount of experience identifying babies that needed extra help. Sandra, the head nurse during the day, was always right on which babies would require our services.

The normal nursery was run by nurses, but the ones who watched the babies most of the time were nursing technicians, who had been doing this for years, and I learned to listen to them, too. Unfortunately, because of new standards, eventually they were all fired and replaced by nurses.

The nurses in the SCN and normal nursery always helped each other when in need of extra hands. At the same time, with the growth of the SCN, the staff was also growing, not only the number of nurses but also full-time RTs, and they helped wherever they were needed.

By the beginning of 1985, things were running smoothly. Tom and I we were not sending babies away anymore, and deliveries continued to increase, so the time we were spending in the hospital also increased. Moneywise we were doing very well, exceeding our guarantee, so we decided it was time to look for a third person. We would only have money for a part-time position, so we decided to look for the right person.

I knew all the fellows who were finishing at Vanderbilt that year, and one of them seemed to be a good fit; she was young, kind, and a good doctor. She was starting a family, and she was a woman, all of which would be a plus for our partnership. I called her and offered her the position, and to my surprise it seemed that that was exactly what she was looking for. Her husband, a young surgeon, was starting a practice in town, so it was the ideal job for her.

We offered her a full partnership owning 20 percent of the practice, while Tom and I owned 40 percent each, and our salaries would be proportional to that. It was a little bit of a gamble for her since even though we were doing well economically, we did not know exactly what we would make in the future. Eventually, it turned out good for her; in her first year she made as much as we did in our first year, and she remained in the group for the next thirty years. Her name was Dr. Elizabeth, but we all call her Liz and sometimes Lizard!

Dr. Liz brought more to the partnership than just more hands. Being a woman, she saw things differently, and I learned a lot from her approach to things. She was very personable, and the nurses loved her. She was also just fresh out of training and had new ideas, which I always welcomed, although many years later I learned that she felt I knew only one way to do things and that was "my way."

The unit continued to grow and expand. Over the next three years, the number of deliveries increased to over 5,000 in 1988, and we had 372 admissions to the unit. As we admitted smaller babies, the length of stay increased, which made our daily census higher. We were busy!

That same year, the new chief of pediatrics, Dr. Charles, brought up in a meeting that the neonatologists were stealing patients from the pediatricians because we were seeing normal out-of-town babies that did not have a pediatrician. I was mad, but I pointed out that a few years back the pediatricians had asked us to see these babies, but we would gladly give them back. Not all the pediatricians were happy, but the decision was made, and these babies would now be assigned to the pediatrician on call for the ER.

This was a blessing in disguise, because we were so busy that seeing normal babies had become an unwelcome chore. By the middle of the year, we decided that we actually needed a full-time third partner, so we hired a fourth neonatologist, Dr. Wendy. She also had a young family, and she wanted to work part time. So after talking it over, we divided the partnership in four, 34 percent for Tom and me and 16 percent for each of them. The calls and the income were divided accordingly. Since the practice had grown, we all kept pretty much the same salary on a lower percent.

Life was good. I was practicing the kind of medicine I had always dreamed of: I got to take care of sick babies, support their parents, share information with the pediatricians, and all this with the full support of the hospital administration. Everything we did was to benefit our patients, whether it was a new piece of equipment or a new therapy. When all else failed, we had the freedom to try new things, many times successfully.

The nurses were very involved; they knew their babies well. We relied on their knowledge to make decisions; our RTs were committed to their jobs, and even the clerks were part of the team. The unit functioned like a well-oiled machine.

At the home front, things were better; money was not a problem anymore. I was on call every third night and every third weekend. I got to see my children more and spend more time at home. As usual Angela was doing a fantastic job; she took care of me, the house, and the children and always did it with a smile! The kids were now ten, seven, and five years old, and early in 1988 we received a big surprise: a new baby girl, whom we named Julia. Not really planned but one of the best things that ever happened to us.

Julia brought us great joy and the need for a bigger house. When she was just four months old, we moved into our new house. It was located about thirty miles away, and it had five bedrooms and three full baths. It was a dream come true! And it would be our home for many years! It also had land around it which allowed us, over the years, to give our kids the things we never had.

What else could I ask for?

Chapter 13

MORE GROWTH AND UNEXPECTED CHANGES

Over the next fifteen years, we continued to grow. In 1988, the hospital deliveries went over 5,000, and the admissions to the SCN reached 350. We were very busy; Dr. Wendy left for a year and was replaced by Dr. Nina, but after a year her husband accepted a position at Vanderbilt, so she returned just in time to replace Dr. Nina, whose husband accepted a position in Texas.

In 1996, we hired another neonatologist, Dr. Sunny, and we distributed the work and income between the five of us. I remained a 34 percent owner all this time, while the other four divided the rest among themselves adjusting it to whatever they needed, since Liz, Wendy, and Sunny all had young families to take care of.

The unit was also renovated the same year, taking over some space that used to belong to the normal nursery. We went from our initial 700 square feet to 1,950 square feet, and the number of beds in the unit went from twelve to twenty-four beds.

We were really busy and spending many nights in the hospital. I was worried about getting burned out. Since I was in charge of making the schedule, I decided to try something more creative so that we could all get longer time off. Taking call every third of four nights was grueling.

After much discussion we decided to try a new schedule; it called for working two weeks every other night plus the weekend and then we would take off completely for a week. For me it was very busy for two weeks, but since the other four were splitting two positions it worked well for them. Having a week off that I could spend with my family was wonderful!

The new schedule provided continuity since there were always two doctors available every week, and we overlapped for a week. For me it was nice to finally spend some time with my family without being exhausted. I think, eventually, my family adjusted to my unusual schedule, too. They would still bring me lunch on my weekend on, and they knew they could count on me when I was off.

The administration was still committed to our patients. As we grew we needed staffing and more equipment, and as therapies changed we requested new medications to be added to the hospital formulary. They were always willing to listen to us, and every time I needed something I knew I could always go to the nursing director's office or the hospital's CEO's office and talk about our needs. Their doors were always open.

We were making money even though we continued to stick to the same principles. We kept our fees low compared to the average fee schedules, and our collection rate was about 70 percent. Eighty percent of our babies had private insurance, and the rest mostly Medicaid. Everybody paid their bills, and we hardly ever had to turn anybody out for collection.

The only problem was that the more we grew the more responsibilities fell on me. Even though Tom and I had agreed to be codirectors, it was obvious that all the responsibility of the operation of the unit had become mine only, as well as all the financial management of the practice. I oversaw our billing clerk; I would collect the insurance checks from her and deposit them. I kept track of the income and paid everybody their monthly share and managed our retirement plan.

I was also the one who had to deal with any problem with the nurses or the RTs. I learned to be a good listener and to be fair to all. Even though I was getting paid well, sometimes all this seemed overwhelming, but on the other hand I got to practice the kind of medicine I always wanted. It all seemed to even out in the end.

A third NICU opened in Nashville at a hospital three blocks from us, and the hospital had remodeled to look like a high-end hotel. Baptist could not afford to be left behind, so the whole maternity floor was renovated. The clean terrazzo floors were replaced by carpet, and the cold tile walls covered with plaster and wallpaper. We started to look like a hotel, too. It was a war to attract patients to deliver at Baptist.

I really did not like the carpet since it was never quite clean, but as long as it did not affect the inside of the SCN, I was fine with the hotel look. From that day on, it seemed like it was a competition between the two hospitals about which one would look more inviting for mothers to come deliver their babies. That went on for the next several years. The attitude was not where it was safer to deliver or which service was better, but which one was prettier and gave more perks.

During these years, we had several therapies we were able to use before our colleagues at Vanderbilt. When the first pulmonary surfactant was being studied, which is used to treat immature lungs in premature babies, I found out we could join the initial clinical trial. This product made a remarkable difference to the care of these babies. In my career it was the single most successful therapy in newborn medicine.

When we decided to join the trial, we did not have to go through several committees to get approval. I just had to present the protocol to the chief of staff, the pharmacy, and the legal department and reassure them that it was safe. We were proud to be the first ones in Nashville to use it. It was a good to be on the cutting edge of medicine. Over the years, pulmonary surfactant became the standard of care all over the world.

We also found a pediatric surgeon who was in private practice, and he joined our team, performing surgery when our babies needed it. A pediatric neurosurgeon and a pediatric orthopedist also joined the staff. We had to send away only very few babies that required specialized treatments; otherwise, we took care of them. It was nice not to split the families anymore.

Early in 2000, we had to deal with a new problem. The pain revolution! In 1995, the Wong-Baker FACES was published; it was a tool designed for small children to express how much pain they had. It was a self-assessment tool; the children had to be able to understand it to use it. JCAH embraced the no-pain campaign and pushed for full pain control. Unfortunately, over the years it became the standard of care not only in children but also in adults; and now they wanted to bring it into the NICU.

Our neighbors at Vanderbilt started treating babies with narcotic drips and keeping them sedated. We could not do that; newborns react to pain like other children do. They cry and become upset. Our nurses knew their babies well, and we used intermittent doses of pain medicine when it seemed necessary. We were criticized much for our position, but our babies were awake, interacted with their parents, and were able to come off respirators on record time.

Unfortunately, all across the country many units used narcotics, and many newborns had to be treated for withdrawal. I always maintained that the faces in the Wong-Baker scale were supposed to be the faces of the patients, not the nurses or the doctors treating the babies! I refused to treat a baby based on my own feelings.

In 2003, we had a massive renovation. Some people in the administration had changed, but the new administration was still committed to keeping the SCN as a priority. The hospital had now reached six thousand deliveries, and they built a whole new wing that would be mostly rooms for mothers after delivery and increased the number of delivery rooms.

The new unit extended into the new building and grew to thirty-five hundred square feet and thirty-two beds. It was what I had always dreamed of! All modern patient units equipped with brand new equipment and more room in between patients. Even though we still had three big rooms, you could see everything from the central desk. The unit had evolved to become a great big family of doctors, nurses, RTs, and clerks working together.

Unfortunately, Dr. Sunny's husband was offered a position in Texas, and she announced she was leaving. It was hard to see her go; her personality was just like her name, and it was always a joy to have her around. We investigated who was graduating from Vanderbilt and found one candidate who came highly recommended by everybody. He was also from Tennessee and likely to stay with us for a while.

So in record time we hired Dr. Kendall. He and Dr. Sunny overlapped for six months, but eventually we were back to five neonatologists. I dropped to 27 percent ownership, and the rest was divided among the other four. It was nice to drop a little on the number of calls, but my administrative duties continued to increase.

Most of the insurance companies were now wanting to negotiate our fees. It was almost a game; they wanted us to give them discounts of different amounts, but eventually all that happened was that we increased our fees, gave the discount, and got paid the same we were getting before. But they could tell their members that they were getting a discount. I spent many hours on the phone and in person negotiating with different insurance companies; I was even coming in on my days off.

Our population was also changing; the third NICU that had opened had taken some of our insured patients. Our collection rate dropped to 50 percent of what we billed. We were now seeing a greater proportion of Medicaid patients but also many more patients; in 2003 the unit admitted 450 patients. In order to keep our salaries constant, we had to play the game with the insurance companies. I calculated then that if we needed to collect $100, we had to bill for $233. It seemed like the cost of intensive care had to increase by more than 50 percent, but actually it had not changed. It was just the insurance companies' game.

The insurance companies as well as Medicaid started to ask for charts to review after we submitted our claims; they would review the chart and decide whether our charges were justified. They started to ask us to write our notes in a specific way. The note we had used for years that communicated the facts of the case, what went on since the day before, the current diagnosis, what changes we made, and what we planned for the future, was no longer adequate.

The clinical value of the notes seemed irrelevant, but the precise justification for the charges was. Our judgment of what level of charge was appropriate was no longer accepted; we had to document exactly what the insurance companies demanded. Our notes went from a paragraph or two to half a page or even a full page, but this change did not improve patient care. just the insurance demands.

We still practiced medicine the same way; one of us stayed in the hospital twenty-four hours and two of us made rounds every morning. One of us was in charge of the intensive care babies, and the other of the intermediate babies. This worked out well; it allowed the intensive doctor to concentrate on the sick babies while the other one took care of those we called growers and feeders and did all the discharge planning.

Occasionally, we would be so busy that the third person would stay and help with rounds, and one of us was always available to come in and help when things got too busy, like the delivery of triplets or two sick babies at the same time. We all pitched in, and there never was a complaint.

For me the most important thing was that we were still very close to our babies' parents, and we maintained a good relationship with them. Since the unit was a big room with many beds, the parents got to meet each other and many times carpooled and supported each other in times of trouble. The nurses were also very involved with the parents and knew their babies very well; we relied on their knowledge to make many decisions. I always say it was like a big happy family!

By 2004, our admissions had grown to close to five hundred a year, and we were also getting smaller and sicker babies. We wanted to hire an additional neonatologist, which would bring us to a total of six. As we searched we found that there were two doctors who might be interested, Dr. Marta and Dr. Mary, both graduating from the neonatology program at Vanderbilt. We interviewed both of them, and both seemed to be a good fit for our partnership. It was hard to decide who would be the best.

One morning Dr. Liz came into my office and told me she had an idea. Could we hire both of them by offering them both a part-time position? This seemed like a good idea; we ran it by the other partners, and everybody seemed to like it. I met with them individually and made them the offer. There was also the possibility that they could increase their time as some of us elected to work less or retire.

Both accepted our offer, and in July of 2004, we had a seven-doctor partnership. We rearranged the time that each wanted to work, and we ended up with Dr. Tom 11 percent, me 17 percent, Dr. Liz 16.5 percent, Dr. Wendy 16.5 percent, Dr. Kendall 17 percent, and the two new ones 11 percent each. We adjusted the schedule so a full-time person would work three weeks on and three weeks off. This was a wonderful idea; we worked very hard for three weeks and then we had three weeks off. The rounds and night calls were adjusted fit the new ownership percent.

When I say ownership percent I mean that each owned the percent of the partnership they contributed to, so the money collected was distributed the same way. Maybe this was not a great business decision since in most partnerships new partners own less and work more, but we wanted to make it fair for everybody. We decided on a monthly salary that was based on the income we expected, and if the practice did better I would give bonuses. But we always kept enough money in the bank for at least two paychecks in case things changed. Luckily, this policy always worked well.

In 2005, the hospital had sixty-five hundred deliveries, and the NICU was admitting over five hundred babies a year. Even though there were seven of us, we were busy; the three-week on and three-week off schedule was a lifesaver. We would never have been able to keep our sanity without it. When we worked we worked hard, spent a lot of nights in the hospital, and lost a lot of sleep. But when we were off we were able to recover and recharge and be ready to do it again. It was the best way to avoid burnout, which many other neonatologists were dealing with.

In January 2002, Baptist Hospital had joined St. Thomas Hospital, part of Ascension Health, and became part of Saint Thomas Health's regional health system. The Baptist administration was replaced by Ascension's personnel, and things began to change.

The first thing was a push to change the work culture; nurses were no longer employees but partners, and the administration began to get more involved in the day-to-day operation of the unit. The head nurse position, which was directly responsible for the staffing and operation of the unit, and the OB/nursery director were replaced by nurse managers, who were more administrators than nurses. What had always been the needs of the NICU reflected on administrative changes was reversed; now the needs of the administration resulted in change at the clinical level.

The acuity of a patient, which had always been a clinical decision taken by the charge nurses, now became a score born of a set of rules that did not always make sense. Everything had to be justified by numbers, and it seemed like the fewer the nurses there were the better. These changes resulted in unhappiness in the nurses; little by little the big happy family became a family of continuous complaints and unhappiness.

The patients became "clients" and the doctors "providers." It seemed like slowly the new culture's purpose was that of dehumanizing the patients and making everything a number. Everything had to be quantified somehow. For the physicians it was all about documenting more and more. We had to document things in the chart to fit a certain code; our notes got longer and longer every day and unfortunately harder to read.

Then the pharmacy started to tell us which medications we should use. I spent hours sitting down with the pharmacy director justifying the medications we used on our babies. As it was mostly an adult hospital, it was hard for her to understand why we would not use the same medications as for the adults. They argued about prices, not about effectiveness! I fought hard for our babies and won many of the battles, but lost many, too.

My life as director of the SCN was getting more and more complicated every day. The administration ignored me, and the nurses expected me to do more. The administrative part of my job was also getting complicated; the insurance companies' demands on how to submit claims got more complicated every day, and each company had its own requirements. Our billing secretary was doing her best, but I had to spend more and more time helping her.

The hospital administration was also changing. From the fourteen administrators we had when I started there were now well over forty. New departments were created in response to government regulations, and many offices were moved to the building at St. Thomas Hospital, which owned Baptist. If I needed to talk to somebody it was almost impossible; it seemed like the only way we could communicate was by email. The open-door policy that we had enjoyed for years was gone. It was hard to run the nursery this way.

All this was taking me away from spending the time I needed with my patients and at home. My three weeks off became the time to take care of all these problems; I felt I was not being fair either to my patients or my family. So I decided to step down as director of the nursery and only keep my duties as the practice administrator. I offered Dr. Kendall the direction of the NICU, and he took it over in 2005.

At home, the children were growing up, and things were changing. Angela, our oldest, was a full-fledged nurse now and had moved out to her own home in Springfield, Tennessee. Laura was married and had moved to Cookeville. Jorge had finished college with an accounting degree but found out he really wanted to be a physical therapist, so he was in college in Florida. Only Julia was still at home finishing high school.

Angela, my wife, had finally more time for herself and had taken a job as a translator and tutor at a local school. Her knowledge of both Spanish and English came in handy. The school she was working at had 62 percent Hispanics, and many did not know how to speak English. She really seemed to enjoyed working and helping these children.

Things were better for a while; at least I did not have to spend as much time in the hospital, and I was able to help our billing clerk more effectively. The partnership was doing well; we had met everybody's salary expectations and got bonuses often.

In 2007, the hospital went through big changes. The administration decided to rebuild the SCN and take over the entire third floor of the newest building. It would increase the square footage from the current thirty-five hundred square feet to twenty thousand square feet and increase the number of beds to fifty. This was a huge increase; I was glad I did not have to be involved in the planning. It kept Dr. Kendall quite busy, visiting other units and deciding which model to follow. The NICU at Vanderbilt had gone for the single-room concept, and I was hoping we would not do that; I felt it isolated the parents and made the nurse's job very difficult.

Thankfully, they decided to go with four-bed pods that could be closed and become more private but still kept the open one-room concept. I was glad.

In September of 2008, we moved into what was finally called the NICU. It was beautiful, and it seemed to be functional. There was a lot of room, and although every bed was separate the four-bed pods kept them close enough for the nurses to watch several babies at the time. The unit came equipped with new monitors, and computer terminals at every bedside. It was nice to be able to look at lab values or X-ray reports right at the bedside.

Unfortunately, this was just the beginning of the end of personal communication in the NICU.

Chapter 14

COMPUTERS AND THE END OF MY CAREER

Computers were supposed to make patient care more efficient. I was glad to see them beside every bed; unfortunately, I never suspected that the electronic age would have such a profound effect on medicine that little by little it would change the way we practice, and this was one of the reasons I retired early.

With President Obama's administration push for the introduction of the electronic medical record (EMR), the hospital started a process of moving away from paper records. The first thing to go was our bedside flow chart. This chart had been the primary source of information for the nurses and physician on a day-to-day and hour-to-hour basis. We relied on it to follow the baby's course through time, and in an emergency all the information was at our fingertips.

Our bedside flow chart contained date, time, and all the pertinent information about the baby: blood gases, respirator settings, laboratory values, vital signs, events, and nurse's notes when necessary. We were able to look at it and figure out problems immediately. This record was at the bedside, immediately available and accurate. It was unfortunately the first thing to go.

The ability of nurses and doctors to communicate through time by means of one simple piece of paper was taken away from us, and the nurses were made to start charting vital signs on the computer, and since the reports from the lab were also available on the computer, there was no need to chart them anymore. The nurse's notes became short, and the narrative disappeared. They were either prewritten choices or very short notations.

Checking out a baby to another nurse moved to the computer screen rather than the bedside. What I had fought for in 1982, when I first came to Baptist, about the nurses transferring care to other nurses at the bedside was destroyed by the stroke of a keyboard. Never to return.

For us doctors also things were changing; we came to the bedside, examined the baby, and then had to go through several computer screens to figure out the vital signs in the last twenty-four hours, as well as the lab work and any nurse's notations. Fortunately, we still had the nurse there to ask questions, and our progress notes and orders were still on a paper chart that we could bring to the bedside. As it had been always my approach, I always went over the orders with the nurse and made sure all was clear.

But things continued to change. For years the nurses prepared and gave any medications we ordered for the babies right in the nursery. There was a locked medicine cabinet, and the charge nurse had the key. Commonly used medications were stocked by the pharmacy. When a baby needed a medication, the nurse obtained it from the medicine cabinet, drew the appropriate dose, checked always with a second nurse to avoid mistakes, and gave it to the baby. It could all be done in a few minutes; it was a four-step process!

This method worked well for us; it was quick and safe. In the thirty years I worked in the NICU, I can only remember one mistake made by a nurse that was of any consequence. Unfortunately, it was difficult for the pharmacy to charge for medications because they had to rely on checking the orders and nurses' charting and match it all with the medication cabinet stock.

Over the years many changes were done to ease this problem. Eventually, we went to a pharmacy medication station that the nurse had to sign in and log the medication obtained. That way the pharmacy could keep track and charge appropriately. But still the process was safe and quick. When I had a baby that needed antibiotics, I could count on the nurse to have them ready by the time I had my arterial line in place.

Emergency medications were also immediately available when we needed them, and the two-person check was a safe and effective way to avoid mistakes.

Unfortunately, what was a quick four-step process, me writing the order, the nurse reading it, then obtaining it, and having a second nurse verify it, became a seven step-process: me writing the order, the nurse checking it, then the clerk putting it in the computer, somebody in the pharmacy retrieving it, who gave it to a technician to prepare, then having the pharmacist verify it, send it up to the floor, and finally the nurse giving it having to trust that it was prepared adequately.

This method was great for the pharmacy for tracking medications and billing, but in practice, the more the steps that were added, the higher was the risk of a mistake happening and even going unnoticed.

In 2012, our billing process also got more complicated. Paper claims were now a thing of the past, and all insurance carriers required us to submit electronic claims. We had to obtain a system that could do that. This proved to be very difficult; teaching our billing secretary at the same time I was actually learning myself was overwhelming.

Fortunately, we survived, and the claims continued to get paid, and we were still making money. Unfortunately, I was spending almost all my free time in the hospital and also spending a lot of time on the phone. Each insurance company had its own rules, and it became more than I could handle. I loved taking care of my patients, but I began to hate my administrative duties.

On looking for an answer I found out that we could sell our practice and let somebody else take care of the billing headaches while we enjoyed practicing medicine. We would receive a salary that would be agreed in advance, and they would do all the billing. There was a large company that specialized in neonatal practices, and I decided to do some research on it.

I talked to several neonatologists around the region who had done that, and all seemed happy with their relationship with the company and felt their salaries were fair. The idea of not ever having to deal with claims and billing again was very appealing to me. It would not affect my partners much, but I was hoping the initial payment for the value of the practice would be a selling point.

I contacted, "The Company," which is how I will refer to it from now on. One very nice representative contacted me, and we set up a meeting. He explained to me that they would examine our practice and determine what its value was and then determine what our salaries would be. I provided him with all the information the same day, since I always kept very detailed records. The Company's policy was not to interfere in the way we practiced medicine as long as our results were within the standards that The Company had. It all sounded wonderful!

I had no idea what our practice was worth! None of the practices I had contacted wanted to share that kind of information. I researched how to determine the value of our practice and found multiple models. I plugged in our values and came up with a price that seemed reasonable. I ran it by all the partners, and everybody seemed fine with it.

Several days later, he came back with an offer. The amount was very close to what I had determined, but the Mexican in me made me try a little haggling. My mother had taught me to never buy anything without haggling!

I suggested a larger amount based on the fact that this was a well-established practice that was still growing, and we wanted to keep our salaries the same as our last year. He took my offer back to The Company, and a few days later he came back with a new offer, much higher than before and offered to keep our salaries at the same level with incentive bonuses if the practice did well. They also suggested we start with a five-year contract.

I took the information back to the partners, and all were happy and agreed on the amount of the offer. Now we were facing the most difficult thing: how to divide the money among us. I suggested that we divide it by the percent of the practice we owned. Almost everybody was OK, but one of the partners who owned a lower percent complained that she had been in the practice longer than some of the newer partners. After much discussion one of the newer partners offered to give up 1 percent, this was followed by everybody offering similar amounts. There was a lot of tension, but eventually we came up with numbers that everybody agreed.

Many years later, I thought about how we distributed the money, and I wish I had been more business savvy. Most practice-selling distributions are made on the basis of the number of years that somebody spent building the practice. Unfortunately, that was not the way we did it. So the younger partners benefited from our ignorance!

We closed in a few weeks, and it seemed like everybody was happy. For me it meant the end of overseeing billing, collecting checks, going to the bank, and keeping track of everything. It also meant that now I had a much larger nest egg, and retiring comfortably was a nice possibility in the future. Unfortunately, more changes were to come.

One of the things that The Company provided was a computer program that would allow us to write our progress notes on a computer and then print them for the chart. It seemed like a good thing. They installed computer terminals in the NICU and connected them to a server in the office. The information in our notes was transmitted to their billing office so that they could determine the charges for each day and we would not have to worry about charging anymore.

It all seemed so nice; I learned the computer program and started writing my notes in it. It took a little longer than our old paper method, but I was OK with it. I would see the baby, do my physical exam, write my orders at the bedside, make sure the nurse understood them, and then go to the computer to write my note.

The notes were not hard to write. When a baby was admitted we had to enter all the identifying information, but after that every diagnosis and treatment was carried on to the next day so that the next day all the information was already there and we just had to update things. Unfortunately, with the way the notes were formatted the number of pages got more numerous every day, and there were times that our daily note would be five or six pages long.

Trying to read a chart to find out how a baby was doing became almost impossible. There were pages and pages of repetitive things, but very few were useful. Since the notes were carried from one day to the other, many times if there was a change and we did not chart it, it would remain in the chart day after day. Many times I would find babies that had come off the respirator days before, but the chart still said they were on it.

The program was excellent for the billing office to determine the charges and for the statisticians at The Company to keep track of treatments and outcomes. But for the patient and for us it did not prove very helpful.

What the computers did over time was to keep us away from the patient and communicate less with the nurses. We seemed to be spending more time at the computer station than at the patient's bedside. Eventually, the company's computers were able to interact with the hospital computers, and the laboratory results and X-ray reports were automatically transferred to the program. The hospital had terminals next to the company's computers, so we did not have to even go to the bedside for information. The only reason to be at the bedside was to examine the baby.

The time we spent with the patient and the nurse was very small compared with the time we spent at the computer station. We were so busy typing into the computer that the nurse manager decided to make the area around it a "quiet area," and the nurses were asked not to bother us while we were typing, and even signs were placed on the wall.

One day I witnessed one of my partners complaining because the nurse came to give her some important information about the baby while she was busy typing her note. Even the attitude of the physicians was changing.

We still wrote our orders on a paper chart; the nurse would check them and then she would pass them to the clerk to type them in the computer. Pharmacy orders went directly to the pharmacy, and the medications brought to the medication station by the pharmacy hours later or sent by pneumatic tube. Many times, the nurses had to wait hours for all this to happen before they could administer them to the patient. It seemed like the more computerized we got, the longer it took to gets things done.

For me getting rid of most of my administrative duties was great, even though I had been named the corporate medical director of our practice, and it was my duty to be the link between The Company's administration and our practice. Most of the time there was not much to do, but I did have to turn in reports every so often and keep track of what the other partners were doing.

Since I had been doing the billing for years, I was very interested in finding out how The Company worked with charges and claims. Our collection percent had not been too bad, but I was curious to see if they had been able to improve it. I was very surprised at what I found!

We did not have to log in charges like we used to; their business office used the data entered in our notes every day, to determine the charges. Then they were sent on a weekly basis to the insurance companies. We never used to bill patients till they went home, so this method was more efficient and provided a better cash flow.

They also increased all our charges by a surprising average of 138 percent. I guess the charges I had negotiated for years for our practice were too low. As a bigger company their contracts were much higher! Unfortunately, I felt, the idea of having charges lower than the competition to help the hospital attract patients was lost.

Some of our most common charges like delivery room care were increased by over 300 percent, and our most common daily charges by 100 percent, so in total what was charged to the insurance companies was more than twice as much as we used to charge.

I never knew what their collection percent was because they did not share that information with us, but at the end of the year on top of our usual salaries we got a bonus. So I knew that they were doing better than what we had done before. It was amazing to me to see that charges could be manipulated so easily.

What bothered me the most was that not being involved in the business part of our practice, I had absolutely no knowledge of how much was paid by the insurances and how much was paid by the patient's family, and most of all I never knew if somebody was referred to a collection agency, which we rarely, if ever, did.

One more way that the computer age had taken us away from our patients was that we had no control over what was done with charges. Many times, in the past, we dropped bills because we knew the family could not afford to pay; but now we had no say in the matter, and we only found out if a parent would call us angry about the bill.

Little by little we were farther away from our patients, their parents, and our nurses.

Parents had also changed; we had a new generation of what I call the Internet-know-it-all parents. They had researched the Internet to find everything they could about their baby's condition, and they would challenge our decisions. Sometimes I would spend hours talking to these parents, finding out where their information came from and how reliable it was and then explaining to them why our treatment plan was different.

I was surprised with the number of sites with misinformation or opinion that was just plain wrong. I used to tell them that the best example was what happens in a horse barn. Each horse owner has his own opinion about how to train their horse, but very few have a scientific base. I had to warn them that what they read was many times just "barn talk."

Eventually, I became very proactive, and I would ask parents on the first day not to go to the Internet. I warned them that it would just confuse them. Most of them would listen, but some would still do it, unfortunately not to their benefit.

The Company did not interfere in the way we practiced medicine, although occasionally our regional administrator would point out how things were done differently at other places. I would always argue that different was not better, and our outcomes were comparable and she would desist. But she seemed to want to be more involved in our decision making.

She would tell me often, "You need to practice Evidence-Based Medicine," and I would always answer, "That is what we have always done!" The Evidence-Based Medicine (EBM) movement started sometime in the late 1990s, and the original definition of EBM was "the conscientious, explicit, and judicious use of current best evidence in making decisions about the care of individual patients." In my mind this is exactly what I was always taught medicine was, but, unfortunately, many administrators have taken this as some sort of cookbook we should follow.

I understand that the practice of medicine has become more complicated over time; the amount of information available is enormous, but it is a physician's responsibility to keep up to what is available in his field of practice. Practical guidelines have always existed; we just did not call them EBM. But every patient is different, and the art of medicine is to know how to apply our knowledge to each patient as an individual. I used to tell the nurses, as a joke, that not all babies read the same book. It is our job to recognize the ones that are different and treat them accordingly.

I always think about those babies that did not read the book; we had to figure out how to take care of them. The best study will always have those outliers that do not respond like the majority. Even the finest study has a "p" value that makes the evidence statistically significant but not true for all. Each doctor in treating his patients should use the scientific evidence available but also, as is often the case, his clinical experience and intuition.

We had a contract with the hospital to provide neonatal intensive care twenty-four hours a day, and in turn the hospital provided us with office space, a billing clerk, and a room where we could spend the night. We always had a good relationship with the hospital. We had the same contract for all the years I had been at Baptist and never had a problem. Unfortunately, The Company had to renegotiate the contract since we were now their employees; the contract did not change much, but our regional administrator started to get involved with the hospital administration and making suggestions that sometimes were not welcome.

Things continued to change; our relationship with the hospital administration became somewhat adversarial. They wanted us to keep patients longer and keep the beds full, and they determined which medications we could prescribe and what respirators we should use. Everything was based on price and what was available through the hospital supplier. Many of the things I had fought for through the years began to unravel.

For years, every time I wanted to talk to the administration, I would just go down and talk to them. Now, I had to email the secretary to get an appointment, and many times they would email me back to find out what I needed. It seemed that instead of talking we were now emailing each other, even though we were just a few steps away.

The use of computers had also changed the way we talked to each other. Sometimes I think that since I was the one to introduce the first personal computer to Baptist Hospital in 1983, I was somewhat responsible for these changes.

One day, I received a phone call from the hospital's CEO; this was surprising to me since we seemed to always communicate by email. He told me he wanted to nominate me to be inducted into The Seton Society. This was an honor I never expected, since the creation of the society in 1991 there had never been a pediatrician inducted. I was flabbergasted and did not know what to say, but I definitely said yes!

A few days later he called me and said I would be inducted into The Seton Society. He told me that the society recognizes and pays tribute to physicians, nurses, health-care workers, and community volunteers who demonstrate excellence in their professions and in their service to Saint Thomas Health and the greater Nashville community.

A few weeks later in a black-tied dinner at the Schermerhorn Symphony Center in Nashville I was inducted and got to meet many previous honorees. This was very exciting; I got to invite my older brother and his wife to join us, and Angela and the children were also there. The parents of one of my old patients got to be the ones giving me the medal; it was a very emotional moment to me. I was asked to say a few words, but I was speechless. All I could say was thank you and mostly thank you to the over eleven thousand babies and parents who had come though the NICU.

Early in 2012, the hospital announced that they were going to implement computerized physician order entry also known as CPOE. This would mean that we would no longer have written orders at the bedside anymore. Now we would write our orders on the computer, and they would go to the computer at the bedside for the nurse to follow, and medications would go directly to the pharmacy.

The only remaining trace of communication between doctor and nurse was going to be taken away. From now on the only thing the physician would have to be at the bedside for was to do a physical exam; the rest was all done at the computer station.

One day, one of my partners asked me if I would look at a baby. She was having trouble adjusting her ventilator. I was happy to do it, so we walked to the bedside. She went directly to the monitor and the very sophisticated ventilator digital screen. I went to the baby's incubator and grabbed the stethoscope so that I could listen to the baby. She said, "Look here. I cannot get his volumes to increase in spite of increasing the pressure."

I insisted on looking at the baby first; as I listened to his chest I noticed that there were breath sounds only on one side. I pulled the tube out a little, and the volumes increased, and the baby immediately improved. It shocked me that she was trying to adjust the ventilator by looking at the computer screen rather than looking at the baby. That was the last straw for me.

My contract with The Company was to get over in October of the same year, so I made the decision to retire. I just could not see practicing medicine in an environment that took away everything I had fought for. Now we talked to computers rather than to each other, we were kept away from our patients, and we now had to cater to the wishes of the administration rather than the needs of our patients.

I gave my partners the news with plenty of time to start hiring a new doctor. In July, there would be several doctors finishing their fellowships, so it was the right time to hire. I talked to The Company, and they agreed to let us hire early so that I could overlap and train the new doctor who was to take my place.

It did not take long to find a candidate; her name was Dr. Alicia, and she was a sweet girl. Even though she had trained in a very different program than we had, she was very willing to learn. I had a good time showing her around and teaching her my philosophy. She learned fast and had good judgment.

When she started taking call on her own she would have questions and would call me on the phone. I think she just needed me to hold her hand because she always made the right decision. The day I left the practice I knew my part of it was in good hands.

Dr. Marta was to become the new corporate medical director, so I passed on all the responsibilities to her, and she moved into my office. This was one of the hardest things I had to do in my life. I had been in that office for a long time; the walls were full of pictures, and there were small mementos from many of my old patients. I had shelves full of books and files of reports from the last thirty years. I put them all in a box, took them to my car, and cried.

This was the end of my career as a neonatologist. I had very mixed feelings. Medicine had changed so much that it was no longer what I had signed up for, but I knew I was going to miss it. It had been a part of my life for thirty-eight years. I was not sure what was next. It was hard to imagine myself not seeing babies, working with nurses, and talking to parents.

I had built the NICU from the ground up, and all of a sudden I was leaving it behind me. Part of me wanted to stay; I even discussed working for the company part time, but we could not come up with a reasonable agreement.

For years I had been working with a corporation that made machines to deliver high flow to the babies. This had been a wonderful thing for our patients; we had been able to reduce the number of babies that required a respirator by using it. We were one of the first units in the country to use it. I had gotten to know a lot of people in that company, especially the CEO Mr. Bill and our salesman Mr. John.

I even testified on their behalf at the FDA when there was a question about the safety of the machine. This was a real learning experience. Dealing with a government agency was sure different, but I felt I needed to show them my safety and efficacy data. I was not about to let them take the machines away from us!

It was an unusual company; they were very involved in making sure the machines were used properly and very interested in knowing the results of their use. I always collected data on our patients, so I was able to provide them with real numbers on how good the therapy was. They would invite me to talk to physicians in other NICUs or to their salesman many times.

It was not infrequent for them to fly me to give a talk to physicians in other NICUs. This was fun, but I could not charge them for my services because anything I collected from the practice of neonatology by my contract would have to go to the company. I was not about to do that, so I always did it for free.

Mr. Bill called me one day and made an offer for me to join their company now that I was retired. I would just have to be part of their advisory board and be involved in promoting their product by presenting my data to neonatologists around the country and also in other countries.

This was an exciting proposition! He could actually pay me now since I did not belong to the company any more. Our association was very rewarding, especially since I believed in the product and had seen it work miracles. I went to many NICUs around the country and met many neonatologists. They also took me to Japan, Mexico, and Colombia. Some doctors were very receptive but some skeptical; it was fun to show them how well the machines had worked for us.

The company was very nice to me; on my first year they had started a yearly award dinner, and I got to be the Physician of the Year for 2013, and our very first baby that used the machine, a little girl by the name of Jada, the Patient of the Year. I, my wife, Jada, and her parents got to fly to Baltimore for the presentation. This turned out to be a very emotional moment for me since Mr. Bill gave what was called The Founder's Award for the work I had done for their company.

His letter said,

To Dr. Jorge Rojas, my friend and dedicated Neonatal physician:

I would like to sincerely thank you for your steadfast dedication to help treat and care for the most fragile of human lives. You had the bold foresight and willingness to adopt new therapies that has allowed hundreds of premature babies to grow into strong and healthy individuals. Your important work has touched so many lives and I want to express my heartfelt thanks on their behalf.

I and many members of our team have had the privilege of knowing you for over nine years. You have been with us from our infancy where we struggled to gain traction, to now, where we have matured in to what is rapidly becoming the Standard of Care. You have traveled with us from Niagara Falls to Mexico City to tell your story about high flow and have participated in important research on our behalf. And even through our toughest time, you helped us pull through the recall and met with the FDA to support our cause. We thank you for being a champion of our technology and for nurturing us just as you have for so many neonatal infants.

All of us appreciate your overwhelming support throughout the years and we look forward to continuing our relationship with you through the next phase. You are a true friend, champion and hero in the neonatal community. As much as we may appreciate your support, I know the infants that you have cared for, and their families, thank you from the bottom of their hearts and the tips of their noses.

My sincerest thanks,
Mr. Bill

Unfortunately, I could not do this for long; I was getting older, and traveling for business became very tiring. Also, I would give the same talk over and over and get the same questions all the time. So after two years, I could not do it anymore. The company had also changed. There was a new CEO and things were different, so I decided it was time for me to stop and enjoy my retirement with my wife at home.

Or so I thought!

Chapter 15

MEDICINE FROM THE OTHER SIDE

Retirement was not easy to begin with. I would wake up every morning and find myself with nothing to do. I had been used to being up at 6:00 a.m. every day and driving to the hospital to see my patients or preparing presentations or traveling, and now I actually had to push myself to get out of bed.

Angela was still working as a translator in the school system, so she would leave early, and I would find myself alone sitting in bed watching television. I was at a loss for something to do. Our children were now gone, two of them married and the other two had moved to live on their own. I felt that we had done well providing for them and helping them be independent, but I sure missed their company now.

I remember very well when my father retired after being a physician all his life. I can see him sitting in the family room in his chair, either reading a book or watching television. It seemed to me that that was all he did, maybe that worked for him, but I did not want to do that.

After so many years of being a doctor, I felt I was what I did. Giving this up was harder than anything; I was not sure who I was now. I visited the NICU many times, but it was just to find out the hard way that I did not belong there anymore. Even though everybody was wonderful to me they had a job to do, and many times I felt I was in the way.

It probably took me six months before I felt I could be useful again. I was lonely; nobody seemed to need me anymore. The sudden lack of structure was exhausting or at least unsettling. For thirty-eight years I had been busy trying to make things better for my family, my patients, their families, and the staff, and now I seemed to have no purpose.

It took a while before I decided that there were many projects around the farm that I had planned on doing in the past, so it was time to get busy. I started to make a sort of a mini-plan for everyday for doing small jobs around the farm, riding, and working with my horses. I tried to keep myself busy and useful, but it took a while before I could say I was satisfied with my life again.

Unfortunately, as we all age, we begin to have health problems. I have been reasonably healthy most of my life and religious about my yearly checkups, but I knew sooner or later I would become a patient and see medicine from the other side.

I have been very lucky to have a wonderful internist, whom I will call Dr. Randy, an old-fashioned doctor; he never switched to EMRs, and he spent lots of time talking to his patients face to face in the room. He felt that the time spent with his patients was more useful than time spent with a computer and that his records were more meaningful than the computer records.

My first encounter with modern medicine from the patient's side was when one night I was awakened by a sharp pain on the left side of my back, which would not subside with anything. I knew this was a kidney stone for sure. I called Dr. Randy, and we scheduled an appointment with a urologist.

As I arrived at the office, the girl at the front desk handed me a computer tablet and told me just to follow the instructions and answer the questions on it. I sat down and started the process; first of all it needed my insurance information, then all my pertinent personal information, my chief complaint, and a description of my symptoms. I filled up all the blanks and handed the tablet back to the front desk.

A few minutes later, a nurse called my name, and told me she was taking me to have a CT scan of my abdomen. I was surprised! I told her I had not seen a doctor yet or had been examined. She told me that with what

I had put in the computer they knew that my most likely problem was a kidney stone, and a CT was indicated. I followed instructions and got a CT scan.

I was brought back to a waiting area and eventually put in a room. The urologist came in, computer in hand, and asked me a few general questions. He apologized for it, but he told me he had to fill in the blanks in my file. He never made eye contact. In a few moments, he told me he had the report from the radiologist, and I had an 11 mm stone lodged in my left ureter.

He told me he would send electronic prescriptions to my pharmacy on record. He was prescribing a medicine that would help relax the ureter and a narcotic for my pain. He would give me three days to see if I would pass the stone, if not it would have to be broken with the lithotripter. He asked me to drink lots of fluids and if I liked beer it was a good choice and then sent me to the front desk for a return appointment and left the room.

I was stunned; he never made eye contact with me, never asked me any other question related to my problem, and never examined me. In my book he had broken all the rules I had always followed in my life as a physician. I could not understand why I had to have a costly procedure worth hundreds of dollars before having a plain abdominal X-ray that would have shown the same and cost less. I learned later that they just followed this protocol on all patients with possible kidney stones.

I picked up my prescriptions at the pharmacy and was surprised that I had been prescribed thirty narcotic pills. I had no idea how I would take that many pills in three days, but I picked them up and went home.

For the next three days, nothing changed; the pain continued, and the pills did not seem to help much so I returned to the office for my new appointment. Again, I was given the tablet and asked to answer the questions; at least I did not have to enter my insurance information again.

The nurse came out again and took me to get a second CT scan. I was surprised, but I did not argue this time. The CT was done, and I went to the waiting area and finally to what used to be known as the examining room. A new urologist came this time. This one I knew; he had his computer, greeted me, and we sat and chatted for a minute until he got the report on the CT. "Bad news," he said. "The stone has not moved; we will have to break it up with the lithotripter." He scheduled me for two days later and handed me a paper prescription for more pain medicine, another thirty pills.

Two days later, I came in to have the procedure done, had another encounter with the tablet, then I met with the anesthesiologist, who again never examined me, then had the procedure done, and went home in the afternoon. The nurse who discharged me gave me some written instructions and a prescription for pain medicine in case I needed it. Yes, another thirty pills!

Even though my problem was resolved, I was amazed that I saw three doctors, and none of them took a history nor did a physical exam. Everybody relied on what was on the EMR I had filled up by the tablet. I had two CT scans done and was prescribed a total of ninety narcotic pills. I don't think I used more than a total of eight pills over the five days and did not use any afterward. I never got the last two prescriptions filled, but they could have certainly made me a fortune on the black market!

My problem was resolved, but the kind of medicine I saw practiced really surprised me. And, I was much more surprised a week later when I got the bill! The total amount for the doctor visits, CT scans, lithotripsy, and anesthesia was $8,422! The two doctor visits were $150 each, for five minutes and no eye contact or even an exam; the CTs $551 each; the lithotripsy itself $6,060; the urologist's fee for the procedure $600; and the anesthesia $360. I asked for a breakdown of the procedure bill, but I never got it.

Interestingly enough, when my insurance paid they only allowed and paid $3,791; my responsibility was only for $568. So the total received by the medical team was $4,359 out of the $8,422 charged. So the charges were inflated by 52 percent. I knew from my experience that this was only the insurance game, but it made the cost of the procedure much higher, and I guess I should have been grateful for the discounts my insurance company had negotiated.

This was just the beginning. In years to come I would have several injuries related to my obstinacy in continuing to ride and deal with horses. I had three rotator cuff repairs, one knee arthroscopy, and the repair of a biceps tear on my left arm. Every single one showed me that the medicine I knew did not exist anymore. Not all physicians were as distant as the urologists; I did get examined sometimes, and many actually made eye contact. But the injuries were usually self-explanatory.

I do remember one of the surgeries, because of the way I was treated by the physician; I'll never forget it. Regrettably, this was only a sign of how much the physician's attitude is changing. I was having outpatient surgery to repair my left biceps. I was admitted to a stretcher; the nurse came in and started asking me questions while she typed in her computer with her back toward me.

I pointed out that I have a heart arrhythmia and that even though it is controlled with medication I wanted to make sure they knew about it. I told her that many times I cannot even tell but my heart rate drops to the 40s. She said OK and left the room. A few minutes later, the anesthesiologist came in and started my IV and told me they were ready to give me some medication. I repeated the warning about my arrhythmia and pointed out that I was not on a monitor, and nobody had actually listened to me. Even though he had a stethoscope around his neck, he looked at me in perplexity and said, "OK, I'll have the nurse listen to you before we put you to sleep" and left the room.

My first impulse was to get up and leave, but Angela asked me to calm down. In a few minutes the nurse came, put her stethoscope on my chest for a few seconds, and told me, "It sounds good to me." Fortunately, all went well, but again some of the basic principles I had been taught and practiced all my life did not seem to be important anymore. As long as everything was entered in the computer a physical exam was secondary.

There seemed to be a desire to complete what the computer asked, but as long as the computer tasks were fulfilled, the patient did not get much attention! Unfortunately, even though many have adopted very sophisticated programs, we still have a key gap in the systems. The original intent of most systems was to capture billing and not to transfer medical information.

Another example of looking at medicine from the other side happened when my wife Angela had to have a kidney stone removed by cystoscopy. As a side note, 30 percent of Tennesseans get kidney stones sometime in their lives, lots of calcium in the water!

This is the way that experience went: We arrived at the surgical facility at 8:00 a.m. as we were instructed. We signed in, and we were called to a small office where a nice lady asked us all about the health insurance, made copies of the cards, and then gave Angela three sheets of paper with forty-eight questions for her to answer and sent us back to the waiting area, where Angela worked frantically answering all these medical questions. I guess they did not have a tablet!

A few minutes later, a nurse called us to her office, and we sat down with her; she took the sheets with the questions, put them aside, and started asking Angela the same questions. We pointed out to her that we had just filled in that same questionnaire, but she argued that now she had to put them in the computer and verify them. So she went through all the forty-eight questions while she typed the answers in her computer. When she was done, she sent us out to the waiting room again.

Another thirty minutes went by and then a nurse came and told us she was going to take Angela to the surgical area and sent me to the waiting area where I would be notified when the surgery was over and she was in recovery. She told us that since she was the case to follow the 11:00 a.m. case it was impossible to predict when that would be.

Angela went with her, was admitted to the surgical unit, given a gown, and placed on a stretcher. The admitting nurse came in with her rolling computer and started asking Angela the same forty-eight questions. When she pointed out that it had already been done twice, she explained to her that she needed to verify all the information in her own computer.

Immediately after, the anesthesiologist came in tablet in hand and started asking some of the same questions. Angela, who is a patient person, pointed out that she had already answered the questions three times.

The anesthesiologist told her that his computer did not interact with the facility's computer so he needed the information.

In the meantime, I went to the waiting area and a nice lady asked me my name and my wife's name and told me her surgery was to follow the case after 11:00 a.m., so it would be a while by the time she was done. She suggested I go to the cafeteria and come back close to noon or so; she took my cell number, and I followed her advice and went to get a cup of coffee, since it was just 10:00 a.m.

I was sitting in the cafeteria, when I heard my name paged over the loudspeaker. I jumped and ran scared to the waiting area. The nice lady saw me and told me that the doctor's office needed to talk to me. I got on the phone, and it was the business office. The lady explained to me that our insurance had only approved part of the doctor's fee, and they needed my reassurance that I would cover the rest before they could start the procedure. I could not believe what I heard. I was rather mad and may have said some not very nice things. I gave her a credit card number, and she was happy with that. The cystoscopy went well, and we went home in the evening.

Every step of the way, the health-care employees were more interested in filling up their computer blanks than looking at my wife; it seemed like as long as the computer form was complete everything should be fine. Whether the patient was taken care of did not seem that important. The business office call was the icing on the cake!

Then the biggest surprise came! A couple of weeks later we got the bill. The facility charge for the six hours Angela was there was $16,256! I could not believe it, even though I knew the insurance game, and I knew we would just have to pay a small fraction. There was a charge for $13,000 for two hours of operating-room time. I wanted to find out what we were paying for. I called the business office and asked for an itemized bill; the nice lady on the phone agreed and told me I would receive it in a few days.

A week later I got the itemized bill. It had a few itemized charges for what appeared to be supplies and medications that totaled $3,256, and two hours of operating room was $13,000 again. I called back and asked what happened in those hours that cost $6,500 an hour. She explained to me that it included the use of the room, its maintenance, and the nurses who were there. Knowing what a nurse makes per hour I could not figure out what could cost $6,000 an hour to maintain! I was told this was the facility fee, but she could not give me an explanation regarding what I was paying for.

This was the case with all my other surgeries as well; the charges were the same. We got a bill that was usually twice of what the insurance paid; we were always told that our insurance company had got us a discount, and we had to pay only a small amount. My problem was that I knew the game: the charges were inflated so that the hospital or doctor could collect what was reasonable, after the discounts.

Hospitals bill patients based on what is called a chargemaster. A chargemaster is a comprehensive listing of items billable to a patient or a patient's health insurance provider. In practice, it usually contains highly inflated prices at several times the cost of actual costs to the hospital. The chargemaster typically serves as the starting point for negotiations with patients and health insurance providers of what amount of money will actually be paid to the hospital. Chargemasters routinely list extremely high prices devoid of any calculation related to cost, but they play a significant role in setting prices for both insured and uninsured patients alike.

Unfortunately, these chargemasters are secret and unregulated; unlike everything else we buy, when we purchase a medical treatment, surgery, or a diagnostic test, we buy blind. We do not know the cost of health procedures before we buy. When we do get the bill, we have no idea what the charges are based on and have no way to evaluate them. Americans pay three, four, sometimes ten times more for medical procedures, operations, and tests than people in other countries.

Chargemaster prices are set by the hospital alone and reflect what the hospital would like you to pay. They are the basis for calculating the discounts given to insurers, and they are generally what is billed to people without insurance. Fortunately, as I learned, they can be negotiated down to much lower levels especially if you offer to pay them in full.

I discovered this from my daughter's experience. She and her husband work for a Christian organization that does not provide health insurance but suggested that they join a health co-op. A health co-op is a nonprofit medical-expense-sharing program. Members share in each other's health expenses. Christian health-care sharing plans enable members to select their own providers and provide access to discounts. The price of procedures can be negotiated by the members beforehand, and in many instances they can be lower to those obtained by insurance companies.

For instance, for a simple office visit a physician may charge $150 with a co-pay of $15 and then could collect another $60 from the insurance company several weeks later, for a total of $75, but may be happy to take $50 or $60 cash on the day of the appointment. Or a hospital may quote the cost of a procedure as $4,000 but may take $1,800 cash in advance with the advantage of being able to shop around other facilities. It is a real example of what could happen if there was genuine marketplace competition.

The cost of medicine has been so inflated by the hospitals, insurance companies, and pharmaceutical companies and has become a game of overcharges and discounts. Many charges have become so far-fetched that they are not credible anymore—from $6,000/hour rooms to $77 gauze or $5 acetaminophen pills. For-profit and nonprofit hospitals declare millions of dollars of operating revenue; unfortunately, little of that money goes to pay for health care.

Total national health expenditures have increased from $443 billion to $3,338 billion from 1982 when I started my practice at Baptist Hospital to 2016. As a percent of the gross national product it went from 5.62 percent to 17.9 percent. So where does this health-care money go?

It used to be that most of the health-care money went to pay for a few administrators who ran hospitals and clinics, doctors, nurses, and other health-care personnel such as dieticians, physical therapists, and RTs. There were also ancillary personnel who helped run hospitals and clinics. Initially, health insurance companies were nonprofit and collected and administered the money from the people to pay for their health care, not much different than the co-ops of today. Medicines and supplies were reasonably priced, and many of them were included in the room charge.

Nowadays, hospital administrations are three times more numerous than they were twenty years ago, and their salaries have increased exponentially. Interestingly, hospital performance metrics show no correlation with CEO compensation, and even the financial performance of hospitals shows no such link. CEOs of small rural hospitals earn salaries and bonuses of just $118,000 a year, while those at the largest urban teaching hospitals earn on average nearly $1.7 million per year. And some CEOs earn considerably more than that.

According to the Fitch Ratings, personnel costs represented 59.2 percent of hospital operating expense, and administrative costs alone account for 25 percent. While the hourly base pay for a hospital executive ranges from $47.34 to $72.39 plus bonuses, an average nurse makes only $27.41 to $ 42.07 an hour. The United States has the highest administrative costs in the world.

Another area where health-care money goes is pharmaceutical costs, which have had a dramatic increase in the last ten years. In fact, US prices for top brand-name drugs jumped 127 percent between 2008 and 2014. While the United States has the largest population and the greatest absolute prescription drug spending as a country, its spending per capita is still significantly higher than that of other countries. Since the United States does not regulate prescription drug prices, Americans are forced to pay the price that the pharmaceutical industry chooses to charge.

The pharmaceutical industry is one of the most lucrative industries in health care. Executive salaries have also undergone enormous inflation. Median pay for pharmaceutical executives amounted to $14.5 million in 2015, much higher than for leaders in any other sector. The eleven largest global pharmaceutical companies made an astonishing $711 billion in profits over the last decade; the same companies paid their chief executive officers a combined $1.57 billion in that period.

Hospitals also spend money on capital expenditures such as monitors, X-ray equipment, and MRIs. As with pharmaceutical products, this industry is outrageously priced. Medical devices make up a relatively small but significant share of national health expenditures. In 2013, the latest year that can be studied with census bureau data, spending on medical devices and in-vitro diagnostics totaled $171.8 billion.

A few years ago, a very good friend asked me if I was interested in joining him in buying into a company that was making neonatal ICU monitors. He gave me all the information on their business plan. I was astonished! Building each monitor cost approximately $250, and a comparable monitor in the market was about $2,500, returning a 900 percent profit. I wish I had joined him, but morally I could not do it.

One more money pit is the health insurance industry. When Blue Cross and Blue Shield (BCBS) companies first pioneered the concept of health insurance in 1929, they pooled the resources of a local community. So the power of everyone's premiums together could afford to pay for the individual members' care when needed. It was a simple concept with enormous benefits, BCBS was a small non-profit company whose only function was to manage the members money. Enrollment in these plans grew from just about thirteen hundred covered lives to three million in the first ten years.

Even though BCBS started as a nonprofit company, many of its branches are now publicly traded. Since then more than forty companies have been created, what started as a community program is now one of the most profitable industries in the United States. In 2014, the health insurance industry grew to $991 billion or 33 percent of total national health-care expenditures. The salaries of CEOs of seventy of the largest US health-care companies cumulatively have earned $9.8 billion in the last seven years. That is an average of about $28.5 million per CEO.

It's obvious why all this has happened if you look at today's health care as pure business, one that is unrelated to traditional health-care values like "caring" or "curing" or "treating." Hospitals used to be clean buildings with the sole purpose of providing care. What I saw happen over the years was the transformation of hospitals into almost high-end hotels. Hospital administrations nowadays seem more interested in marketing than providing care. The more amenities the better! There is more interest in hospital consumer surveys than the actual care given. Another costly item!

The other side of medicine does not look pretty to me; I have been lucky to have an internist who still appreciates the value of the history and the physical exam, but it seems like many others have forgotten their value. The EMR has pushed physicians and nurses to be data-entry technicians, and little by little we are losing the ability to communicate with each other.

On top of that, medicine has become a business not a service anymore. Prices are outrageous, and even doctors often do not know the costs of the tests and procedures they prescribe. Hospital administrators, pharmaceutical company CEOs, and data managers decide which way things must go, and doctors, nurses, and other health-care personnel are just spectators.

I can see the day when I will just open an app on my phone, email my symptoms to my doctor's office, and a computer algorithm will decide what treatment I need, then send an electronic message to my pharmacy, and they will deliver my medication to my front door, or schedule me for a CT scan, or a surgical procedure. All immediately charged to my insurance carrier, who will negotiate discounts on my name and charge my portion to my credit card. No need to see a doctor!

Chapter 16

MEDICINE UPSIDE DOWN
ARE WE BETTER OFF TODAY?

Well. . .the last statement in the previous chapter was what I hope never happens, but it feels from the way medicine is proceeding, my fear may not be unfounded! In 1976, Jerrold S. Maxmen, published a book titled *The Post-Physician Era: Medicine in the Twenty-First Century*. In his book he predicts a future in which doctors will be rendered obsolete by a collaboration of computer systems and what he calls a medic, whom nowadays we would call a physician assistant or a practitioner.

Some of the developments he predicted are actually occurring. Innovations in communications technology, education, professional roles, and administration are having a profound impact on the medicine of tomorrow. Some of the policies and programs that have been put in place by government and administrators are failing to yield the results they promised. We do have options to affect the future; I hope we recognize them and correct the trajectory of medicine.

When I began my voyage, medicine was a service; I went to medical school because I wanted to help people. I was following the example of my grandfather, my father, and my brother, who dedicated their lives to do exactly that. I did not become a doctor to make money and be rich. All the doctors in my family did well; they all had a comfortable life along with their families. I did well, too. But I always tried to be reasonable in my charges and cognizant of my patients' needs; until all was taken out of my control by the business of medicine.

Medicine for me was a service we provided to our patients and their families. We went to medical school, and we trained to be able to recognize human disease and how to cure it, and sadly sometimes realize we could not change it. We learned through our training how to relate to patients, how to obtain a good history, and how to probe with our words and find the problems. We learned how to explore the human body and find signs that would help us determine what was happening. We learned to be doctors!

I learned through my life in medicine that we need other people to do our job; doctors would not be worth anything without nurses to help them, without therapists to guide them, and even without administrators to support them. But I learned over all, that medicine starts with the patient, and what we do should always be guided by what the patient needs.

Why do I think that medicine is upside down?

When I started my practice at Baptist Hospital in 1982, things were the way they were supposed to be. I was hired to start an NICU, and the administration was willing to support all the needs of our patients. Whether it was equipment, medications, or personnel, all we had to do was make our case and things happened. The benefit to the patient was everybody's number-one priority. We had to decide what we could afford and what alternatives were there, but always with one goal in mind: that our patients be taken care of.

We charged for what we did, using an easy system of codes. We submitted to the insurance company what was called a reasonable and customary charge, and we got paid. Coding was simple and reflected the service we provided no more no less. The insurance company paid the percent agreed by their contract, and the patient paid the rest. If the bill was large and the patient could not pay, we had the option of either taking smaller payments or drop it. It was simple!

The first thing that happened was that competition among hospitals created an environment that pushed hospitals to change from service-oriented somewhat sterile facilities to hotel-like places with more and more amenities. There was a war to become the best-looking hospital in the area, but still provide a service. Regrettably it resulted in increased cost. Then the patients became clients, and the doctors turned into providers, and anybody who worked in the hospital became an associate.

Unfortunately, these so-called providers and associates had no say anymore on what was needed for the care of their clients. The hospitals became businesses, and the decisions shifted to the administrations. The purpose became to make money, and new administrators had to be hired; from 1982 to 2012, hospital administrations grew by 200 percent or more.

Insurance companies suffered the same problem; they went from administering their members' money to a very lucrative business. Between the demands of insurance companies to pay claims and government regulations, the game of charges and discounts started, and the coding revolution began. The government and the insurance companies demanded more documentation and claims with appropriate, more complicated codes.

Coding became an industry by itself. Since 1977, the global medical community accepted the ICD system; since then it started to be used by insurance companies to code diagnosis and procedures. This system has been upgraded constantly, and currently the ICD-10 has over sixty-eight thousand codes, and continues to be modified. This structure was supposed to help with the reimbursement process. Fewer denied claims and physicians and health-care providers paid for specific services faster.

Unfortunately, what it did was create a whole new business: Medical Coding!

Medical coding was the transformation of health-care diagnosis, procedures, medical services, and equipment into universal medical alphanumeric codes. Many colleges and universities started offering coding training, and, eventually, in 1988 the American Academy of Professional Coders (AAPC) was founded. The AAPC was established to provide education and certification to coders working in physician-based settings. Eventually, it expanded beyond outpatient coding into hospitals.

Medical billing and medical coding are two of the fastest growing jobs in the health sector. Coders are not only involved in billing, but their skills extend into medical auditing, compliance, outpatient practice, and practice management. Currently, billing and coding expenses constitute about 18 percent of all US health-care expenditures—around $470 billion dollars a year.

In any well-functioning health-care system, sound administration is required to ensure efficient operations and quality outcomes. In the United States, however, the complex structure of health-care financing has led to a large and growing administrative effort and cost.

Then came the government: In 1996, Congress passed the Health Insurance Portability and Accountability Act also known as HIPAA. This legislation sets data privacy and security provisions for safeguarding medical information, and it resulted in exaggerated changes that added more to the cost of medicine. If you visited a doctor's office you were given a two-page paper about HIPAA, most of which ended in the trash. Also, when you signed in, your name had to be kept secret, so special removable line sheets had to be purchased, and your last name could never be said out loud!

In 2009, the American Recovery and Reinvestment Act (ARRA), also known as the Obama Recovery Act, was signed into law. Within the Act there was the Health Information Technology for Economic and Clinical Health Act (HITECH), which promoted the adoption and meaningful use of technology in health care, allocating $25.8 billion dollars for health information technology investments and incentive payments This gave birth to the worst thing that ever happened to health care: the EMR.

In 2013, the HHS, modified HIPAA in accordance with guidelines set by the HITECH Act concerning the responsibilities of hospitals and physician's offices. As electronic records technology became a part of health care, there were new potential places for a breach to occur. So it also increased penalties for HIPAA compliance violations to a maximum of $1.5 million per incident. These regulations have been extremely impactful; many offices and hospitals have spent millions of dollars to meet these requirements and are still trying to keep pace. Entire costly compliance departments with compliance officers were started.

Lamentably, the EMR's initial goal was not to communicate medical information, but to facilitate billing and coding. It became a very successful tool for hospitals and outpatient services to capture all billable items, collect statistics, and follow specific elements. The EMR was touted as a way to provide better care: barriers between silos of care would fall, duplication of expensive testing and interventions would be avoided, and physicians could leverage the power of patient data.

Disappointingly, a recent *Medical Economics* survey found that more than two-thirds of physicians are dissatisfied with their EMR's functionality, and more troubling, nearly half said that patient care was worse since implementation. These findings have been echoed by countless studies associating EMRs with physician burnout, early retirement, and, ironically, poorer care.

The author of a recent article in the *New England Journal of Medicine* entitled "Getting Rid of the Stupid Stuff" points out how EMRs have large numbers of pointless tasks that benefit nobody. The promise that collecting Big Data would benefit health care has not materialized.

In the past medical and financial record theft was rare. But since the advent of EMRs and either web or cloud-based records, information theft has become a major problem in the medical industry, which has continued to add to the cost.

I can't say that the EMR is all bad; it can be appropriately used for education, scheduling, electronic intake forms, and digital refills, but it can never take the place of a good history and physical exam. The interaction between the physician and his patient cannot be digitized. There are things that are easily integrated into an EMR, such as vital signs, lab values, or measurements, but others are so subjective that they require a narrative that is not available on most EMRs.

After I retired I learned firsthand how poorly EMRs communicate information. I had been doing research on thirty-nine small premature infants that I treated in our NICU. I decided to follow all of them till they were discharged home; many of them were in the hospital several weeks. When I went to review their charts, I found out how worthless EMRs were. Everything was fractionated: lab values, X-rays, nurse's notes, and doctor's notes were all on different screens. Trying to make sense of them was almost impossible, and there was no narrative, only prewritten sentences that made no sense. The daily doctor's notes were six to seven pages long and repetitive. I spent months going over the records and piecing out the information for my research. So much for communicating information and portability! EMRs do not support the complex documentation requirements of human interaction.

Worst of all EMRs have not come cheap; implementing an EMR system could cost a multiphysician practice over $160,000. As of May 2015, the Centers for Medicare and Medicaid Services (CMMS) had paid more than $30 billion in financial incentives to more than 468,000 Medicare and Medicaid providers for implementing EMR systems. Data breaches and security threats are becoming more common and are estimated by the American Action Forum to have cost the health-care industry as much as $50.6 billion since 2009.

The use of EMRs has also created the need for another group: health-care information technologists. The number of workers in IT-related jobs has increased as EMR technology has been adopted. Hospitals and physician's offices have found that following EMR implementation, reimbursement has increased not as a result of up-coding or more generous reimbursements per charge, but rather due to a significant increase in the number of ancillary procedures billed. What used to be included in a patient room charge or operating room charge can now be billed separately item by item.

Nurses and doctors have become data-entry technicians. The focus has changed from accurately obtaining information from the patient to filling endless forms of data. It has become the way to communicate between health-care personnel, rather than communicating directly with each other.

Another area that has changed is the multitude of supplies and medications that have to be used by hospitals and physicians. Supplies are expensive. Hospitals and physicians' offices have to rely on third-party distributors who can buy in bulk and store large amounts of supplies. This cost is in then passed on to the consumer. Medical supplies account for 17 percent of total hospital expenses. In addition, supplies are an increasingly large component of health-care spending, with the Association for Health-care Resource & Materials Management predicting that supply costs will exceed labor as hospitals' greatest expense by 2020.

Moreover, because of government and hospital rules and regulations, supplies are wasted in enormous quantities every day. A study published in *The Journal of Neurosurgery* in 2016 exposed how the public hospital wasted an estimated $968 per neurosurgery, amounting to a total of $2.9 million over one year. The National Academy of Medicine estimated that the US health-care system squanders $765 billion a year. All supplies (even unopened ones) are discarded at patient discharge due to CMMS requirements and hospital infection prevention precautions.

We have created a health-care industry in which a large proportion of the money goes to pay for tiers of people, equipment, and supplies that have very little to do with care. Over time it has become more and more expensive but disappointingly with very small benefit to the patient, which is in fact the reason the health-care industry exists.

Probably the most expensive and problematic area in health care is the health insurance companies. As I discussed in the previous chapter, the complexity of the system has made medical billing into an extremely difficult process; the interaction between physicians, hospitals, and insurance companies is not only complex but adversarial. One side is looking for the higher number of codes that can be billed while the other side is looking for ways to delay or reduce reimbursement.

In the meantime, the government and the insurance industry continue to change how things are billed. Many new business models on health-care reimbursement have come and gone, and none have made a difference, and sometimes they have made it worse. We started with the traditional fee for service, which had been the rule for centuries, then moved on to health maintenance organizations (HMO), managed care plans (MCP), bundled payment plans (BPP), accountable care organizations (ACO), pay for performance (P4P), value-based health care (VBH), and now the patient-centered medical home (PCMH). All these models have done nothing but to make health insurance more complicated and more expensive.

A recent study on the costs of billing and reimbursement showed that when synthesizing the available data, their analyses indicate that costs totaled $470 billion annually in the United States. Of this 80 percent represents additional costs when compared to a simplified financing system. If costs were paired to that of benchmark systems, system-wide savings would exceed $350 billion per year. That is savings of almost 75 percent!

In the last thirty years, there have been amazing advances in medicine, but they have been overshadowed by the transformation of medicine from a service to a business. We have more knowledge now, but we are farther away from our patients than we have ever been. I do not believe we are better off today than we were then.

What is the solution? It is already happening; many physicians are rebelling against the system and many new practice models are emerging, models that give the patient and the physician more independence. Health co-ops and concierge medicine are good examples. Companies are beginning to administer their health benefits themselves and are beginning to use on-site clinics for their employees. Many other physicians are electing to go to straight fee for service. All these changes are an effort to bypass the insurance companies and charge for what they do and not for how many codes they can use.

The public is also changing; younger generations are electing to use acute care centers and walk-in clinics to stay away from complicated physicians' offices. Convenience is winning over endless computer forms and packed waiting rooms.

Computers and electronic records are helpful when it comes to scheduling and storing laboratory results and X-rays. Some of these things can be digitized, but medical records should continue to include meaningful observations and findings. In medicine there is no substitute for exhaustive histories and detailed physical exams. Data without interpretation are facts without meaning.

The digital age has introduced artificial intelligence, algorithms, automated products, and massive data storage, but they will not substitute critical thinking based on knowledge and experience. Recently IBM's Watson computer failed to reliably understand and interpret patient medical records. Watson can research the literature faster and more extensively than a human and provide treatment choices, but it has been shown to not always make the correct decision.

Medical research produces enormous amounts of information every year. In 1996, fewer than five hundred thousand new articles were listed in PubMed; in 2014 there were more than 1.4 million. But medical fields have also shrunk; there are now more specialties and subspecialties with more limited fields. Keeping up with the literature is not that difficult anymore; journal reviews and Internet searches are easily accessible. Rather than spending time entering useless data into computers, physicians should be able to read and keep their knowledge up to date.

If medicine is to be a business, the answer to our current problems should follow a true business model. It should be 100 percent transparent. We should know what we are buying, what it will cost, and who will do it cheaper and better. There is nothing wrong with competition. Health insurance should have the same transparency and should be able to compete not only within states but across state lines. Coding should be simplified, and government agencies should be allowed to negotiate drug prices, not allowing drug companies to set prices indiscriminately.

As the Hippocratic oath says, physicians should continue to teach and nurture new generations. The best teachers are those who genuinely care for their patients, peers, and trainees, and show respect for the personhood of each patient. Many patients may be disillusioned with health care, but they still want the same things: to be listened to and to be cared for. Despite meaningful additions to diagnostic tools over the past thirty years, it is still true that no matter how many tests are ordered, an accurate diagnosis is elusive without a solid history and a careful physical examination.

I am lucky enough to still have Angela, the love of my life, and my children Angela, Laura, Jorge, and Julia, and my grandchildren Molly, Micah, and Madelynn. I am also fortunate to still be in contact with my old partners and nurses who have traveled with me on this voyage. Finally, I am also blessed to have seen many of my patients grow up and still keep in touch.

I hope this book helps someone; I am probably not going to see the medical system we are creating. I am just sorry for my children and grandchildren. Thank God I'm on the way out and not on the way in.

ABOUT THE AUTHOR

This is Dr. Rojas's debut book. Although he has written multiple scientific papers and a medical-text chapter, this is his first book. He writes this time about his own life through the medical world. Dr. Rojas is a retired physician after forty years of practice, but he is also a husband, father, and grandfather, a musician, and an avid horseman. This book is literally his life, but rather than an autobiography, this book highlights the changes in health care during his career. Born and raised in Mexico City, he has lived in the United States for forty-five years. He currently resides with his family in middle Tennessee.

Made in the USA
Lexington, KY
22 December 2018